MUSCLE MANAGEMENT

MUSCLE MANAGEMENT

A new and revolutionary technique for maximizing athletic potential and dealing with sports injuries

Elizabeth Andrews

Illustrated by Peter Cox

Thorsons
An Imprint of HarperCollins*Publishers*

Thorsons
An Imprint of GraftonBooks
A Division of HarperCollins*Publishers*
77–85 Fulham Palace Road,
Hammersmith, London W6 8JB

Published by Thorsons 1991

1 3 5 7 9 10 8 6 4 2

A catalogue record for this book is available
from the British Library

ISBN 0 7225 2168 5

Typeset by Harper Phototypesetters Limited,
Northampton, England
Printed in Great Britain by The Bath Press, Bath, Avon

Contents

Preface

The purpose of Muscle Management is to introduce the athlete and trainer to Applied Kinesiology in its simplest form, as a means to better performances. I do not presume to claim any of these techniques as my own, nor to be the first to describe them to non-chiropractors and non-osteopaths. I am translating the material (already made available by John Thie) into sports terms, and sharing some of the techniques I have used. Beyond these, Applied Kinesiology should never be used on its own nor without the background knowledge of a chiropractic, osteopathic or medical practitioner.

I have tried to eliminate medical language and concentrate on simplicity. For those who need the reassurance of medical back-up before they even try a new technique, I have included Dr Rodney Adeniyi-Jones' explanation of muscle testing in the Appendix.

I have purposely omitted much technical data from the disciplines that Applied Kinesiology embraces, such as Acupuncture Five Element Law, complicated nutritional advice and manipulative techniques. They are of course extremely relevant, but the athlete should seek a specialist Applied Kinesiologist for these. However, what I have included is simple and safe and works brilliantly and will, I hope, empower athletes to greater heights in performance.

I would like to express my thanks to George Goodheart DC, founder of Applied Kinesiology, John Thie DC, Sheldon Deal DC, John Bandy DC, Nancy Joekel, Dr Rodney Adeniyi-Jones, Daphne Tomlin MC and all my friends, dancers, musicians and athletes who come to me for help and who inspired me. I also have to thank my mother Tanya and husband Bernard for unfailing encouragement, patience and good humour and Sue Lake for her support and hours of typing.

Note to readers

Before following the advice given in this book, readers are urged to give careful consideration to the nature of the athlete's particular health problem and to consult a competent physician if in any doubt. This book should not be regarded as a substitute for professional medical treatment and while every care is taken to ensure the accuracy of the content, the author and the publishers cannot accept legal responsibility for any problem arising out of the experimentation with the methods described.

CHAPTER 1

Introduction to muscle testing

This is a book about muscle management. It does not replace training but it does help make the most of it and keep athletes out there and at it, and on track for success! It is much harder to train a muscle that is 'switched off' (for whatever reason) than one which is switched on and working normally when required.

The techniques presented here are both preventive and restorative. They catch stresses, strains and potential weaknesses before they become serious problems or before accidents happen. They often work when nothing else will (especially when there is still a residue of hesitancy and doubt in performance following the best of modern medicine and physiotherapy). The techniques work because we use the body itself to tell us what it needs by muscle testing.

There have been a great many books written about sports injuries and retraining. This is not just another one of those, and you will find nothing here about strapping and bandaging, and nothing that conflicts with conventional physiotherapy techniques of 'rest, ice, compression and elevation'.

These safe methods are different and have been developed over twenty-five years by American chiropractors. We often use relief or 'help' points which are not at the site of injury but which nevertheless speed the healing process and so can be used by the injured athlete at home, before and after training and together with the modern medical treatment that the doctor provides. The techniques are complementary to modern medicine, not alternative and as such, they broaden the possibilities available and provide a personalized programme of self-help once s/he has learned the relevant points.

Despite their simplicity, the techniques have been welcomed by those doctors, nurses, physiotherapists and trainers who have had the courage to try them. At the very least they are harmless and helpful.

The techniques are drawn mainly from chiropractic, osteopathy and traditional acupuncture, but most of all from the brilliant work of George Goodheart, DC, who formulated Applied Kinesiology, members of the International College of Applied Kinesiologists (ICAK) who helped develop it and especially John Thie, DC, who made the basic technique available to a wider readership through his book *Touch for Health*.

There are over fifty reasons why muscles become 'weak'. These can be roughly divided into a triad of mental, physical and chemical causes. Few problems have only one cause; the other two points of the triad are almost always affected to some degree. Once you find the right combination of points to work on, the effect is instantaneous and very pleasantly surprising. Real 'Muscle Magic' at your fingertips! It is very exciting to see how strength and balance return to normal and know that you have done it yourself. And so fast!

Here you will find the most common relief points which will deal with 80 per cent of the niggling sort of problems that athletes encounter. The other 20 per cent are way beyond the scope of this book and need advanced techniques which are constantly being updated. For these you will need to see an Applied Kinesiologist. Don't be dismayed by all this. To use the contents of this book you just need to use your hands and work wonders! It's fun, it's easy and it's safe.

CHAPTER 2
Athlete failure

Why, despite training hard, do some people simply fail to reach their potential? They are apparently doing everything right and yet they fail, their technique is 'all over the shop' and nothing 'flows'.

In this book I go into details about why muscles 'switch off' just when they are needed, and how old injuries can inhibit present performance - especially in the areas of accuracy, speed of reaction and co-ordination - even though the athlete is not consciously thinking of the original accident. In other words, I show how to clear out old rubbish! Later in the book I will also help with the mental pressures besetting athletes.

On the question of diet, I have kept myself to few comments beyond saying what each specific muscle needs so that the likely nutritional needs specific to an athlete and his or her sport can be worked out. I do not go into supplements or medical dietary advice best left to dieticians, as I am assuming we are dealing with people who are basically healthy. I do, however, suggest foods that contain specific vitamins because solid food will be chewed more thoroughly and therefore be assimilated more thoroughly. 'You are not what you eat but what you absorb,' (to quote Goodheart). Few people bother to chew pills and that lessens their absorption and effectiveness.

I also outline how to test for food sensitivity, which will cause muscles to go weak. This is not Allergy Testing, but it will give you clues about where to look for an elimination diet if that is necessary.

This book does not discuss training methods or the pros and cons of quantity versus quality or types of training, equipment or shoes, etc. It is for you and your trainers to know what works best in a particular sport; and what an athlete's physical and mental make-up and potential are.

So, having got that out of the way, why do athletes fail? Answer - muscle imbalance caused by the 'big three' muscle stressers, which are: mental stress, physical stress, chemical stress. One or all of these can give rise to the body 'switching off' muscles and causing them to feel weak, wobbly and unsure.

Think of the triad of health again. Pain leads to mental stress by impinging on clear thinking. Fuzzy, negative thinking, holding back and worrying mean poor digestion, so poor assimilation of vitamins and minerals and high toxicity in the system.

Chemical stress, due to wrong foods, poor assimilation and dehydration and mineral loss through sweat, leads to muscle starvation and muscle fibres being clogged with waste products, which means that they fatigue and operate poorly. Poor response is disappointing and leads to trying too hard and this is when accidents happen and pain is caused.

In a nutshell, athletes fail because they make one or more of the above mistakes and get in the downward spiral which compounds itself as it goes. Only when the whole body machine is working perfectly can smooth improvement be hoped for, good co-ordination, injury avoidance and the confidence to reach for success and full potential, and satisfy that hunger for winning that is part of every sports enthusiast. How do you do it? By asking the body what it wants. How do you ask? By muscle testing. But *please*, before you dive in and test, read the next chapter (Chapter 3) first. It will save you a lot of puzzling and mistakes.

CHAPTER 3

How to use the book and switch on to strength

This is perhaps the most important chapter in this book, for without reading it you will fail to get results.

1 It is vital that you are accurate about muscle testing.
2 You need two people to muscle test. (I will assume you, the reader, are testing an injured athlete.)
3 Be precise in following the illustrations about positioning the athlete's limbs. As often as possible I have given alternative test positions for each muscle so that you can use the most comfortable one, or try several to make sure your findings are correct – but only test two times at most or you will cause fatigue and the muscle will then seem weak.

Unfortunately, you can't remove a muscle, test it and put it back like a spare part of a car! Nor can you ever really test one muscle at a time. All you can do is make sure that one muscle you think you are testing (the agonist or prime mover) is the one doing the main work, and the synergists (or helpers) are put at a disadvantage. There are bound to be other muscles helping because there is almost always a back-up system of synergist muscles that have a similar action. If the main muscle is weak, the athlete will twist to try to use these synergists, so **precision position** to get the right one. Sloppy testing gives sloppy results!

There are two types of muscle action important to the athlete:

1 Action – as when you leap off the ground or push or lift – called Gamma II.
2 Reaction – such as when your muscles take up the shock when you land after a jump, or catch a ball – called Gamma I.

Gamma II uses the brain because the athlete decides to lift or leap.

Gamma I uses the spinal reflex response which is instinctive and so potentially faster.

The test position for both is the same. It is a question of who initiates the test (the tester or the athlete) and therefore which nerve pathway is used. Either pathway can be upset in a sports injury, so you need to test both.

To test Gamma I, place the limb accurately and ask the athlete to hold the position. Wait 1-2 seconds and then you push against the hold. The athlete reacts instinctively to your push to hold the limb in place.

To test Gamma II, place the limb accurately as before. Ask the athlete to push first, then you push in the opposite direction to overcome the athlete's push.

How strongly should you test?

This type of muscle testing is not the same as is taught in hospitals, although it does come under their definition of Grade V testing. Here we are not testing gross strength or range of movement. (For a further discussion of this see page 187.) Nor is it competitive testing (i.e. can the athlete or you beat each other?), nor is there a right- or left-handedness about it because you are testing too lightly for this to come into play. Simply, does the muscle switch on when you ask it to?

You are looking for *quality* of reaction, not quantity. The test is done within a 2-3 second time-frame and ½"-2" (1-5 cm) range of motion or depth of travel as you push, not more. How does it feel? Is the reaction immediate, spongy, jagged, painful, etc? Anything other than an immediate lock against the tester's light pressure counts as weak.

In other words, you test slowly and lightly but deliberately, and not too deep, using the same pressure each time, almost as if you were listening to the response. If you want to test other fibres of a large muscle, you vary the starting position, not the depth of test. Beginners may find a little difficulty at first, but it is quite easy to attune yourself to the athlete's feel. (The more people you test the better you get.) Generally, the more aggressive the athlete, the *lighter* the test. It's not a tug of war and any heavy testing will invite competition – which is something an athlete does almost instinctively. Compare right and left muscle tests. This is important because, although you are testing too lightly for right- and left-handedness to be important, it will give you an overall feel of how the athlete reacts to your testing.

Don't forget the muscle must have a stable base to push against. This varies according to whether the athlete is standing, sitting, or lying because gravity and support change relative to body position. Make sure the muscle is strong in the position in which it is used in the sport, not just when s/he is lying on the treatment table.

How do I know which muscle to test?

First, assess the problems and the pain by getting answers to these questions. They are useful reference points later.

1 Where is the pain? Does it feel deep or at surface level?
2 Does the pain move about or stay in one place?
3 What kind of pain is it? Shooting, stabbing, radiating? (Often a muscular and structural cause.) Searing, burning? (Often a chemical cause.) Throbbing, pounding? (Often to do with circulation.) Ache? (Often a chronic or residual rather than an acute problem.)
4 What caused it and when does it happen now? (Be precise about the body position of the athlete when it happens.)
5 What makes it worse and what relieves it? Does it hurt without movement?
6 Is it getting better or worse? Suddenly or gradually?
7 How long has it existed? Has it happened before, or something like it happened before?

8 Has there been an operation there or near by?
9 What precisely does it stop the athlete doing?
10 What type of warm-up and warm-down exercises are done?
11 What are the flexibility and range of motion like?
12 Is s/he over-trained or over-competed?
13 Is adequate endurance training done?
14 Are the muscles used equally on both sides of the body or does the athlete's sport use one limb much more, or even exclude the others from movement?
15 On a scale of 0-10, if 0 is no pain and 10 is the worst that can be imagined, how bad is it now? At its worst? At its best?

Give a score out of 10 and make a note of it because it is hard to remember how bad a pain was when it's gone.

Get the athlete to answer these questions as carefully as possible. They give useful clues about where to look and how to solve the problem.

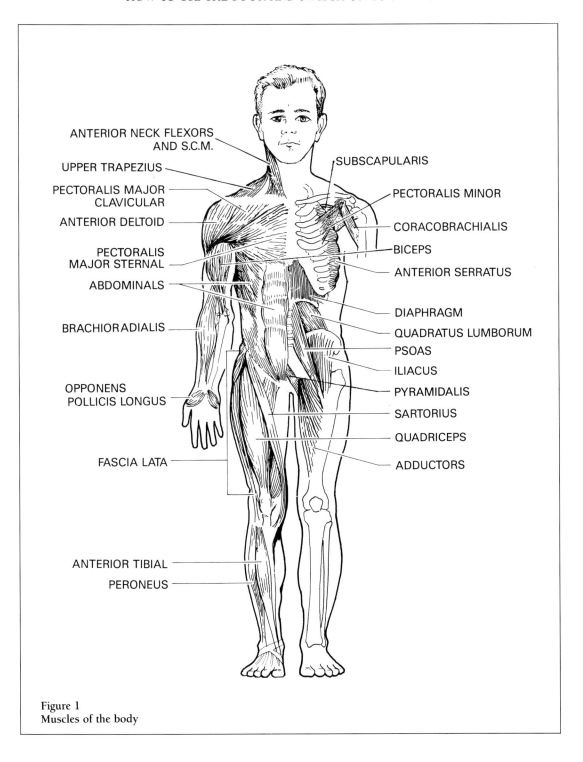

ANTERIOR NECK FLEXORS AND S.C.M.

UPPER TRAPEZIUS

PECTORALIS MAJOR CLAVICULAR

ANTERIOR DELTOID

PECTORALIS MAJOR STERNAL

ABDOMINALS

BRACHIORADIALIS

OPPONENS POLLICIS LONGUS

FASCIA LATA

ANTERIOR TIBIAL

PERONEUS

SUBSCAPULARIS

PECTORALIS MINOR

CORACOBRACHIALIS

BICEPS

ANTERIOR SERRATUS

DIAPHRAGM

QUADRATUS LUMBORUM

PSOAS

ILIACUS

PYRAMIDALIS

SARTORIUS

QUADRICEPS

ADDUCTORS

Figure 1
Muscles of the body

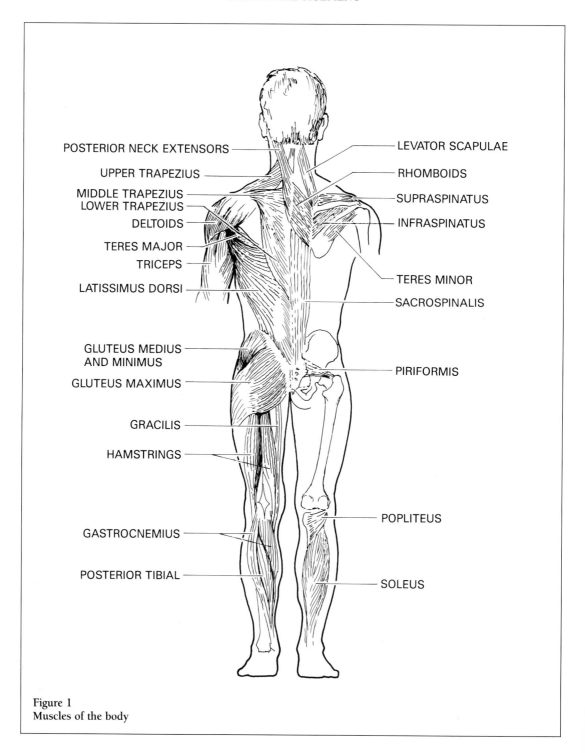

Figure 1
Muscles of the body

Now find the muscle

1 Consult the diagram in Figure 1 and identify the muscles that most nearly approximate the same area as the pain. Don't forget there are often several layers of muscles with fibres going in different directions.

2 Look up the information for the specific muscle, given in Chapter 4. Test it by copying the positioning in the accompanying illustration as closely as possible. If it is strong, reacts immediately and easily and does not cause more pain, then test others around it that have a similar action – and not forgetting the ones that have

the opposite action which could also be the cause of pain now.

Remember, a pain can be caused because a muscle is slack and switched off (because of trauma), causing imbalance with its opposite number (or antagonist) which has now to take up that slack. This can cause spasm or cramp. Or vice versa, a muscle has gone into spasm through over-use and won't relax, so its opposite number can't contract fully and therefore has to try and work at half strength and, not surprisingly, it complains by being painful! (See Figure 2.)

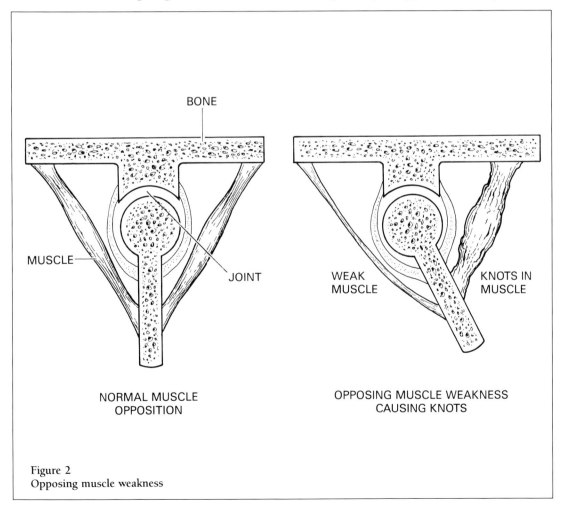

NORMAL MUSCLE OPPOSITION

OPPOSING MUSCLE WEAKNESS CAUSING KNOTS

BONE

MUSCLE

JOINT

WEAK MUSCLE

KNOTS IN MUSCLE

Figure 2
Opposing muscle weakness

3 It is also well worth testing the same muscle on the opposite side of the body (i.e. test both left and right latissimus dorsi) or a similar action, anti-gravity muscle back and front (i.e. abdominals and sacrospinalis). The presence of pain doesn't mean you shouldn't test, although of course you proceed with caution and don't test repeatedly. Often the pain will disappear if you or the athlete touch the 'help' points at the same time as the muscle is being tested. This means those points need attention and are directly related to the problem.

4 Strengthen the muscles according to the points on that page. Massage the points shown as solid dots (see Figure 3) hard for 30 seconds (but do not massage over any broken skin). *Hold* the points shown as open circles (see Figure 4) for at least 30 seconds, lightly enough just to stretch the skin. You may even feel a pulse. If you do, wait till it is slow and even. You do not have to be 'pin-point' accurate like an acupuncturist. Three fingers held lightly over the area is sufficient.

Don't worry if you feel nothing; just wait for a couple of minutes anyway. Continue till all the muscle points are done. N.B. When you hold the acupoints, make sure you hold the same hand as foot, i.e. right hand with right foot. Do not mix them!

5 Reassess the pain levels and retest. *Do not* let the athlete try out the muscle in full action yet. Be content with immediate pain reduction and greater strength. Let it settle and if necessary try the muscle again tomorrow. **Healing takes time!**

6 If there is still a residue of pain next day, go to the section on Extra Techniques in Chapter 6.

7 If there is no pain then the athlete may gently use this muscle again. Retrain it first before using it to full capacity. A muscle doesn't work by itself - the whole body has to rebalance itself in the light of its new found strength (as any dancer will tell you). Never forget that pain is there as a warning and should not be ignored or 'worked through' - that only stores up trouble for later.

8 If, after trying the extra techniques, there is still a high level of pain, the athlete should go and see a doctor, chiropractor or osteopath. The muscle may have been more damaged than you realized. Safety first! These techniques do not replace injury treatment, they are aids to rehabilitation, injury prevention and muscle improvement.

9 Use the 'help' and diet points which are given for each muscle as a preventive measure to keep the athlete fit longer and as part of the 'warm down' routine after training to help the body clear away excess lactic acid in the muscles. This will pay handsome dividends in reduced stiffness and aches as well as improving posture, balance and muscle strength.

What happens if I do it wrong?

Very little. If you mistakenly weaken a strong muscle by mistreating the points, the athlete's body will quickly put it right. The worst you can do is massage too hard and cause bruising.

What are the pitfalls of manual muscle testing?

Tester faults

1 Poor positioning of tester and/or athlete. Both of you must be as comfortable as possible. An awkward and unbalanced tester can't do a good test. Think about your position and hand holds before you pick up an athlete's limb. Don't have more than one joint between your testing hand and the muscle as you will then be testing joints, not muscles. Above all don't put your stabilizing hand on the muscle you are attempting to test!

2 Too heavy, too long, too deep testing and too many repetitions which will tire a muscle already under stress. Be clear about what you are doing

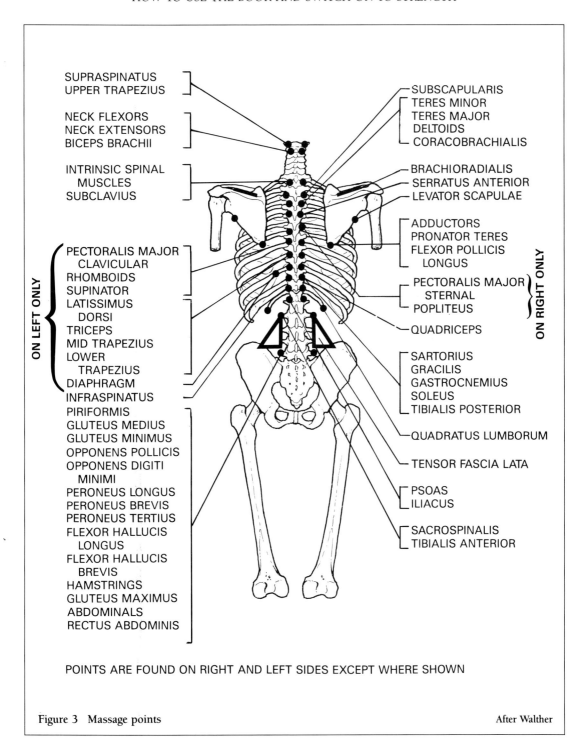

SUPRASPINATUS
UPPER TRAPEZIUS

NECK FLEXORS
NECK EXTENSORS
BICEPS BRACHII

INTRINSIC SPINAL
  MUSCLES
SUBCLAVIUS

ON LEFT ONLY

PECTORALIS MAJOR
  CLAVICULAR
RHOMBOIDS
SUPINATOR
LATISSIMUS
  DORSI
TRICEPS
MID TRAPEZIUS
LOWER
  TRAPEZIUS
DIAPHRAGM
INFRASPINATUS
PIRIFORMIS
GLUTEUS MEDIUS
GLUTEUS MINIMUS
OPPONENS POLLICIS
OPPONENS DIGITI
  MINIMI
PERONEUS LONGUS
PERONEUS BREVIS
PERONEUS TERTIUS
FLEXOR HALLUCIS
  LONGUS
FLEXOR HALLUCIS
  BREVIS
HAMSTRINGS
GLUTEUS MAXIMUS
ABDOMINALS
RECTUS ABDOMINIS

SUBSCAPULARIS
TERES MINOR
TERES MAJOR
DELTOIDS
CORACOBRACHIALIS

BRACHIORADIALIS
SERRATUS ANTERIOR
LEVATOR SCAPULAE

ADDUCTORS
PRONATOR TERES
FLEXOR POLLICIS
  LONGUS

PECTORALIS MAJOR
  STERNAL
POPLITEUS

QUADRICEPS

ON RIGHT ONLY

SARTORIUS
GRACILIS
GASTROCNEMIUS
SOLEUS
TIBIALIS POSTERIOR

QUADRATUS LUMBORUM

TENSOR FASCIA LATA

PSOAS
ILIACUS

SACROSPINALIS
TIBIALIS ANTERIOR

POINTS ARE FOUND ON RIGHT AND LEFT SIDES EXCEPT WHERE SHOWN

Figure 3   Massage points

After Walther

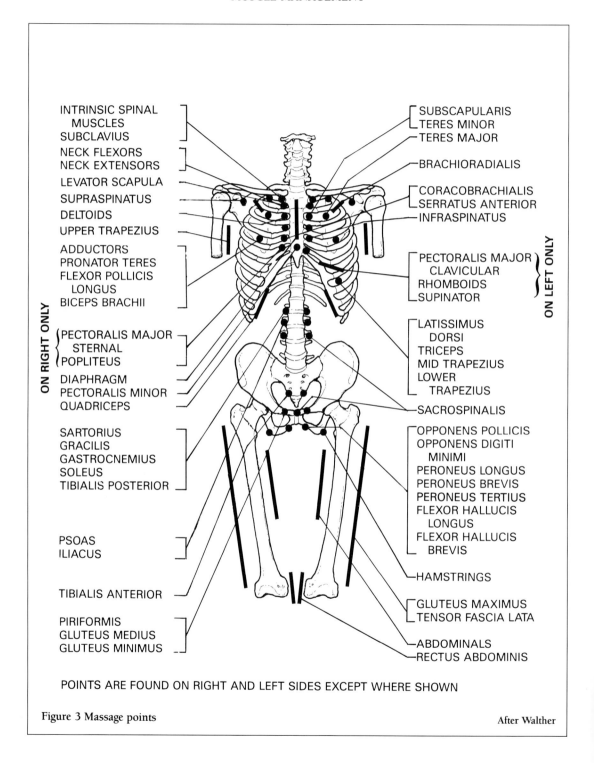

INTRINSIC SPINAL
   MUSCLES
SUBCLAVIUS
NECK FLEXORS
NECK EXTENSORS
LEVATOR SCAPULA
SUPRASPINATUS
DELTOIDS
UPPER TRAPEZIUS
ADDUCTORS
PRONATOR TERES
FLEXOR POLLICIS
   LONGUS
BICEPS BRACHII

ON RIGHT ONLY

PECTORALIS MAJOR
   STERNAL
POPLITEUS
DIAPHRAGM
PECTORALIS MINOR
QUADRICEPS

SARTORIUS
GRACILIS
GASTROCNEMIUS
SOLEUS
TIBIALIS POSTERIOR

PSOAS
ILIACUS

TIBIALIS ANTERIOR

PIRIFORMIS
GLUTEUS MEDIUS
GLUTEUS MINIMUS

SUBSCAPULARIS
TERES MINOR
TERES MAJOR
BRACHIORADIALIS
CORACOBRACHIALIS
SERRATUS ANTERIOR
INFRASPINATUS
PECTORALIS MAJOR
   CLAVICULAR
RHOMBOIDS
SUPINATOR

ON LEFT ONLY

LATISSIMUS
   DORSI
TRICEPS
MID TRAPEZIUS
LOWER
   TRAPEZIUS
SACROSPINALIS
OPPONENS POLLICIS
OPPONENS DIGITI
   MINIMI
PERONEUS LONGUS
PERONEUS BREVIS
PERONEUS TERTIUS
FLEXOR HALLUCIS
   LONGUS
FLEXOR HALLUCIS
   BREVIS
HAMSTRINGS
GLUTEUS MAXIMUS
TENSOR FASCIA LATA
ABDOMINALS
RECTUS ABDOMINIS

POINTS ARE FOUND ON RIGHT AND LEFT SIDES EXCEPT WHERE SHOWN

Figure 3 Massage points

After Walther

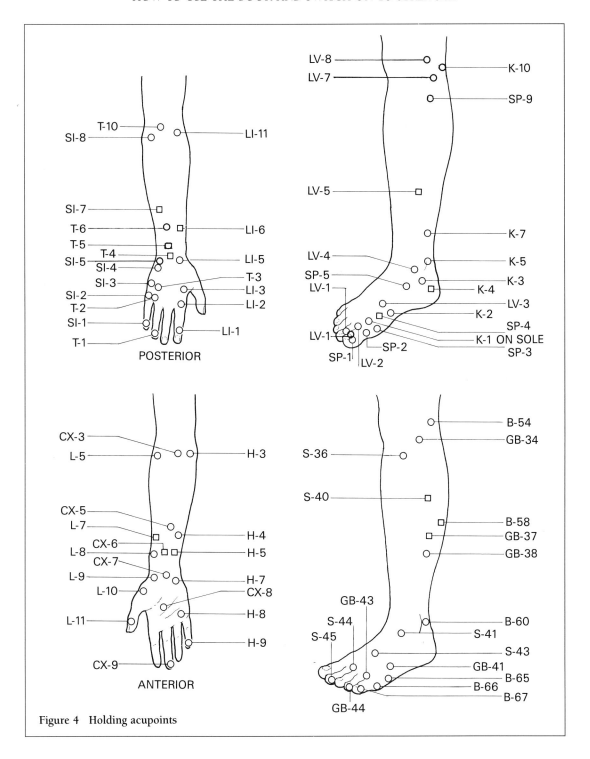

Figure 4   Holding acupoints

and feeling and do it efficiently. **Twice is enough.**

3 Making the athlete hold his/her position for a long time, whilst you make up your mind how to test, leads to needless fatigue. Work it out first, then test.

4 Squeezing the part of the limb you are holding will cause pain and the muscle will go weak as a reaction. Watch out for rings and bangles digging in, too!

5 You test the wrong muscle or your own muscle is weak and the athlete picks it up and 'surrogates' (see Extra Techniques in Chapter 6 for this).

6 Your testing is not objective. Because you so much want a muscle to be strong, will-power can alter the muscle test result. If you suspect this might be happening, deliberately think about something else while you test.

7 Asking the athlete to 'Try to hold,' or 'Try it again,' instead of just saying 'Hold,' or 'Hold up/in/out/down,' as appropriate. Asking someone to try does not imply that they will succeed. It confuses the brain by asking for effort but not to succeed. This is a 'mixed' message and so the muscle test will inevitably be weak, no matter how much effort is expended.

Athlete faults

1 The athlete will use synergists to help himself/herself. This is unconscious cheating. The first priority of a human being is survival. Knowing at an unconscious level that the muscle is weak, the athlete will 'survive' by using other muscles to do the job by moving, twisting slightly or bending another part of the body, using the synergist back-up system provided by Nature. Watch out for this. In particular, be careful when the athlete starts to learn the testing positions. He or she will 'helpfully' hold the limb up - but of course it will be unconsciously in the best, strong position and not the best test position; so I repeat, *you*

position the limb and position accurately according to the illustrations.

2 The athlete will hold his or her breath whilst you test. This can change the result! Make sure they are breathing normally or breathing out gently. As a last resort, make them talk as you test.

3 The athlete will hook a joint round another limb or the edge of the testing table to give support. Unhook the limb and retest.

4 The athlete will forget to concentrate. Too often when they say 'I don't understand what you want,' they mean that instinctively they know they can't do it, so they don't understand physically. Frequently, too, they will lift the head to look and see what you are doing, or close the eyes to concentrate better. Do not allow this as results can be altered. Physically show the athlete what is wanted and retest.

5 Subconsciously the athlete knows what will strengthen their body and will frequently instinctively place their hands over the relevant reflex points for that muscle. Watch especially for crossing hands on the chest or putting hands behind the head. Remove them and retest.

6 Just occasionally the athlete may be so worried about a muscle that they will 'quit' on the test, or will the muscle to be weak. Make them talk about something else while you retest. This is, however, very rare - most athletes can't wait to get better. If it does happen, read Chapter 7 on 'The will to win.'

As you can see from the above list, it pays to be pernickety at first till you both get the hang of it. Best of all, find someone who can already test or go to a 'Touch for Health' class (see Useful Addresses at the end of the book). Above all, *don't* dive in and test without first asking the athlete's permission and making sure there is no known reason why you shouldn't test, such as a pinned joint, plate, replacement hip or other such problems. Don't assume such things will be obvious. Always ask.

Food sensitivity

There has been much in the international press recently about athletes and drug abuse. Few people realize that drugs are not the only things we put in our mouths that change performance.

What I am talking about here is food sensitivity. At its worst it becomes severe allergic reaction and possible collapse. Obviously this last is a medical state which must be dealt with by doctors. However, the level of reaction can be quite small and go unnoticed unless the athlete is looking to eliminate all possible hindrances to performance.

Just as a muscle that is weak because of a lack of a vitamin (or mineral) will strengthen when the athlete eats that vitamin (or food containing it), so the reverse is true.

Any food that requires more energy from the body to assimilate it than it actually provides, will cause a net deficit and thus muscle weakness, be it the finest quality food, clean, fresh, raw, organic, etc. The same is true of overdose. The body will weaken to that, too. Ignore all the propaganda and advertising about a particular food or food supplement and ask the body concerned, i.e. the athlete's body, by using muscle testing – is this good and strengthening to eat today?

Food sensitivity is a strong suspect if the athlete feels drowsy or lethargic, breathless, lacks concentration, gets headaches, itchy eyes, runny nose, has mood changes after meals or at specific times of day.

How to test

1 First test the fourteen muscles as advised at the end of Chapter 4. Also make sure that there are no other muscles weak that are specific to the athlete's sport.
2 Have the athlete chew a teaspoonful of food or food supplement (or hold a sip in the mouth if it's a liquid or sniff the substance continuously) and retest the muscles.
3 Any food that makes the muscles weaken is a

food sensitivity so don't eat it just before a match! Most commonly this will be a food the athlete eats every day and may be slightly addicted to, because they feel a quick lift (only to feel depleted later).

4 This type of testing only tells you about the athlete's reaction today – not next week or any time later. The food must be in the form that the athlete normally eats, i.e. cooked, not raw, potato, as cooking can change the chemical formula.

The food must also be the brand (or make or country of origin) that is normally eaten because of sprays and additives. If the athlete doesn't normally eat the peel of the fruit, for example, peel the fruit first. Sprays may penetrate into fruit, but some fruits have some constituents only in the skin.

5 The mouth must be washed out between each food test. I find it helpful, if there are multiple tests to be done, to put a small amount of the food on one of the other main nerve complexes, such as the navel, instead of the mouth – it saves washing the mouth out, but is not so accurate in giving results with the muscle test.

I also find it useful to relate the food to the aches and pains the athlete feels, taking the muscles near the pain and retesting with both possible helpful supplements and possible food sensitivities. A supplement that helps may relieve the pain felt as the muscle is being tested, whereas a food sensitivity may increase the pain.

Nutritional supplements

Vitamin A Liver, dark green leafy vegetables, melon, tomato, eggs, carrots.

B Complex Liver, yeast, wholegrains, eggs, fish, nuts, sunflower seeds, organ meats (offal).

B_1 (*Thiamin*) Yeast, brown rice, wheatgerm, soya, sunflower seeds, eggs, liver, pork, offal.

B_2 (*Riboflavin*) Mushrooms, liver, offal, skimmed milk, yeast, whole grain, soya, peas, eggs, beef, chicken, pork, cottage cheese, spinach and green leafy vegetables.

B_3 (*Niacin*) Fish, brown rice, chicken, almonds, liver, beef, offal, mushrooms, yeast.

B_6 (*Pyridoxine*) Soya, liver, pork, beef, cod, salmon,

yeast, oranges, bananas, wheatbran and wheatgerm, sunflower seeds.

Vitamin C Green pepper, brassicas (sprouts and cabbage), melon, water melon, citrus fruits, strawberries, tomato, rosehips, green leafy vegetables.

Vitamin D Eggs, fish, liver, oil, offal, sunlight.

Vitamin E Soya oil, corn oil, wheatgerm, peanuts, margarine, mayonnaise, salmon, kale, all meats, parsley, eggs, peas.

Vitamin F Unsaturated fatty acids in plant oils.

Vitamin G (see B2)

Iodine Kelp (seaweed), seafood.

Calcium Milk products, dolomite, raw grains,

brassicas. With a deficiency, avoid foods containing oxalic acid such as rhubarb, cranberries, coffee, chocolate, and purple fruits such as plums.

The most common foods that cause sensitivities:

Grains – wheat bran or gluten in the wheat, so try wholemeal *and* white bread, oats, barley, rye, rice, corn (maize).

Milk products – milk, cheese (all types), sheep's and goat's milk, yogurt.

Meats – beef, pork, lamb, chicken, turkey.

Fish – freshwater and sea fish, shellfish.

Potato family – potatoes, tomatoes, eggplant, peppers.

Brassicas – cabbage, sprouts, broccoli, calabrese, cauliflower.

Fruits – apples, lemon, oranges, strawberries.

Nuts, peanuts and soya products

Coffee (including decaffeinated), chocolate, Indian and Chinese tea

Tartrazine, monosodium glutamate

Alcohol – especially red wine. Include beer and whisky if there appears to be a grain sensitivity.

CHAPTER 4
Muscles and muscle management

Muscles in groups according to area

1 **Muscles of the neck**
Sterno-cleido mastoid and scalenes; splenius and semispinalis; upper trapezius; levator scapulae.

2 **Muscles of the shoulder girdle**
Subscapularis; infraspinatus; supraspinatus; rhomboids; deltoids (anterior, middle and posterior); pectoralis minor; teres minor; teres major; coracobrachialis.

3 **Muscles of the arm, wrist and hand**
Biceps brachii and brachialis; brachioradialis; triceps brachii and anconeus; supinator; pronator teres and pronator quadratus; thumb and finger flexors and adductors; hand flexors and extensors.

4 **Muscles of the front abdomen**
Abdominals and pyramidalis; pectoralis major (sternal and clavicular); diaphragm.

5 **Muscles of the back**
Anterior serratus; middle and lower trapezius; latissimus dorsi; sacrospinalis or erector spinae; quadratus lumborum.

6 **Pelvic muscles**
Psoas; iliacus; piriformis; gluteus maximus, medius and minimus.

7 **Muscles of the front and inner thigh**
Quadriceps; adductors and pectineus; sartorius; gracilis.

8 **Muscles of the back and outside thigh**
Hamstrings; popliteus; tensor fascia lata.

9 **Muscles of the shin, ankle and foot**
Peroneus; gastrocnemius; soleus; anterior and posterior tibials; toe extensors and flexors; adductor hallucis.

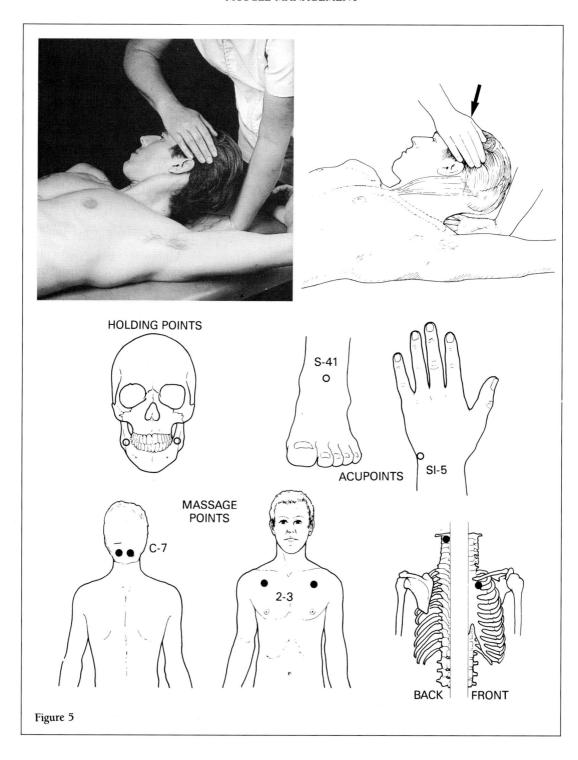

Figure 5

MUSCLES OF THE NECK

Neck flexors (sterno-cleido mastoid and scalenes)

Description

These muscles are very important in the neck. Not only do they connect the back sides of the skull to the breastbone and collar-bone, thus bending the head forward or to the opposite side (depending on whether one or both sides are contracted), but they are also very important in keeping the head looking forward as you walk or run. The muscles in the front of the neck are not normally as strong as the muscles at the back of the neck because the head naturally falls forward when you are upright and so has to be held back (unless you actually want to bend forward).

The nerve supply to the sterno-cleido mastoid (SCM) is unusual in that it is double - this makes it an important muscle for the balance and self-righting mechanisms of the head in relation to the body - essential when you consider that proportionally the head is the heaviest part of the body (see Chapter 6 under Gait mechanism).

How to test SCM

The athlete lies on his or her back and the head is lifted. Immobilize all other shoulder and arm muscles that might help by putting the athlete's hands above the head. Pressure is put on the forehead to push it back down on the table. This tests both sides simultaneously.

(*See Figure 5.*) To test one side at a time, lift the head then turn it to one side (60° if you can). Pressure is put on the temple to push the head back down to the table. Watch that the athlete does not try to turn or twist the chin to change the angle and recruit other neck muscles. When you press down, place your other hand under the head - not touching it - to break the fall if the muscle is weak, rather than banging the head down on the table. If the muscle is very weak, the athlete will be unable to hold their head up for more than a few seconds, if at all.

How to test Scalenes

The test position for the deeper neck flexors, the Scalenes, is very similar to sterno-cleido mastoid (SCM). The athlete lifts the head centrally from a lying position, as for SCM, but tucks the chin in and turn the head 10° to one side. (Watch that there is no sideways tilting of the head.) Pressure from the little finger side of your hand is put on the forehead to press the head directly back to the table (and not in alignment with the 10° turn of the head). Watch for the athlete turning the head further round to try to use SCM or the opposite scalenes.

Other muscles to test if SCM is weak: pectoralis major clavicular (PMC), upper trapezius, sartorius, soleus, gastrocnemius, gracilis.

HELP

Massage Points

1 The second space down from the collar-bone between the ribs, in line with the nipples.
2 Either side of the spine at the very top of the neck (lamina of C-2).

Points to hold

1 On the side of the jaw, on a line directly under the corner of the eye.

2 Acupoints S-41 and SI-5. S-41 is on the top of the foot in the centre of the ankle crease. Hold it at the same time as SI-5 which is on the side of the wrist on the bump of the end of the ulnar bone and below the little finger.

Diet

Since this muscle seems to have associations with the drainage system for the head and also with the sinuses, it is important to check for any possible food or airborne allergies if there is constant weakness. Eating seafood which contains iodine will help, but for general congestion problems in the head and neck area all the B vitamins are needed, especially B_6 and B_3. Yogurt will also help, but otherwise cut down on dairy products to lessen mucus.

Sports problems

This muscle is very badly affected by whiplash type injuries and 'cricks' in the neck, both of which make it difficult to turn the head and give great soreness, shoulder tension and headaches. Sports injuries are mostly from overuse or falls onto the head or wrenching from riding, gymnastics, diving, rugby, judo and boxing, or always using the muscle one side as in swimming when breathing to one side only.

However, pain can be referred to the neck from digestive or other internal organ malfunction. Weak neck flexors can also cause vertigo, tinnitus, allergies and vision problems. One very surprising cause of neck muscle weakness is too tight shoes, where the toes are hard up against the front of the shoe. Tension and worry can tighten the shoulder muscles and with them neck muscles such as SCM. If this is the case, turn to Chapter 7, which discusses stress management.

Exercise

Isometric neck exercises, head rolls.
Weight training – neck exercise machine, sit-ups.

Neck extensors (splenius and semispinalis groups)

Description

These muscles are usually stronger than the neck flexors because they have to hold up the heaviest part of the body – the head – against gravity. They are made up of many strands of muscle which could almost be said to be a continuation of the complicated rigging and cross-hatching and layers of muscle that support the entire spine at the back. Here we will concentrate on the main group, which hold the head back and which contract when the head is put back to look directly above and up to the side.

How to test

(*See Figure 6*) The athlete lies face down with shoulders and elbows bent 90° so the hands are held off the table. To test both sides together the head is lifted off the table and pressure is put on the back of the head to push it back onto the table. To test one side at a time turn the head as far as possible to the side and pressure is put on the side of the head (and against the ear) to push the head directly back onto the table. Watch for sideways bending when the athlete tries to recruit other muscles. As with neck flexors, it is kinder to place your hand between (but not touching) the head and the table to cushion the fall of the head.

Other muscles to test if neck flexors are weak: upper trapezius, pectoralis major clavicular, sartorius, gracilis, soleus, gastrocnemius, piriformis.

HELP
Massage points

1 Underneath the collar-bone, directly above the nipple and in the space between the next two ribs below.

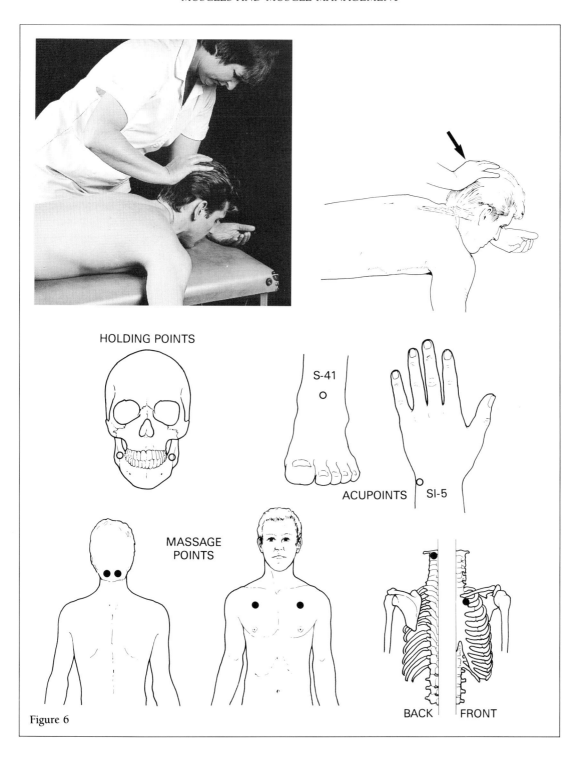

HOLDING POINTS

S-41

ACUPOINTS | SI-5

MASSAGE
POINTS

BACK | FRONT

Figure 6

2 At the very top of the neck either side of the spine where it meets the skull.

Points to hold

1 The ramus - on the lower jaw on a line directly below the outer corner of the eye.
2 Acupoints S-41 and SI-5. S-41 is on the top of the foot in the centre of the ankle crease. Hold it at the same time as SI-5, which is on the side of the wrist on the bump of the end of the ulnar bone and below the little finger.

Diet

These muscles react badly to stress and to a lack of B vitamins (especially B_6 and B_3) and organic iodine.

Sports problems

These muscles are used in all overhead work such as serving in racket sports, as counterbalance in weight lifting, basketball, volley-ball, netball and where the head needs to be thrown back to see or breathe as in snooker, butterfly stroke, handstands and flickflacks, rugby scrums, American football, wrestling, archery, swimming.

These muscles, together with upper trapezius, are also very prone to tighten in response to stress or, conversely, tire when there is prolonged looking down to the ground. Because the head is the heaviest part of the anatomy and furthest from the ground, neck muscle integrity is vital to balance, in conjunction with eyes and ears and can affect the whole set and angle of the head. A knock-on effect would be pelvic and sacral problems, also sinus headaches.

EXERCISE

Isometric neck exercises.
Weight training - neck machine, back extension.

Upper trapezius

Description

The upper division of the kite-shaped trapezius muscle is found on the top of the shoulder running from the tip of the shoulder, the outer end of the collar-bone and the top of the shoulder-blade to the base of the skull and all the neck vertebrae. It raises the shoulder girdle and bends the head and neck to one side when only one is contracted. Right and left work against each other to hold the head and neck centrally on the shoulders.

How to test

(*See Figure 7*) The athlete sits and tilts the head so that the ear is as near as possible to the shoulder. Pressure is put on the shoulder and the side of the head to prise them apart. Watch that the athlete does not try to turn the face away from the side of weakness.

Other muscles to test if upper trapezius is weak: levator scapulae, neck flexors and extensors, rhomboids, pectoralis major clavicular.

HELP

Massage points

1 The top 3″ (8 cm) of the front of the upper arm in the groove between the muscles.
2 Up against the skull bone at the top of the neck.
3 Between the second and third ribs next to the breastbone.
4 One inch either side of the most prominent bone at the back of the base of the neck.

Points to hold

1 Half-way between the corner of the eye and the top of the ear.
2 Acupoints K-7 and L-8. K-7 is at a spot found if you measure a hand's width up the inner shin

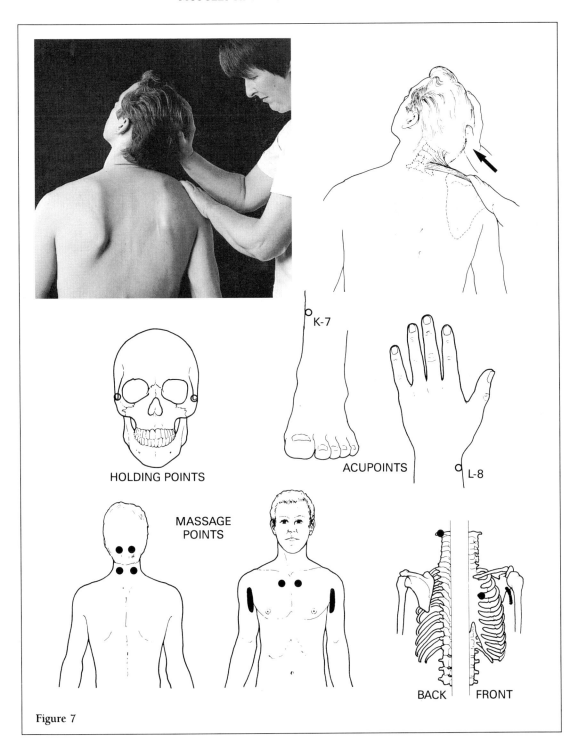

HOLDING POINTS

ACUPOINTS

K-7

L-8

MASSAGE POINTS

BACK FRONT

Figure 7

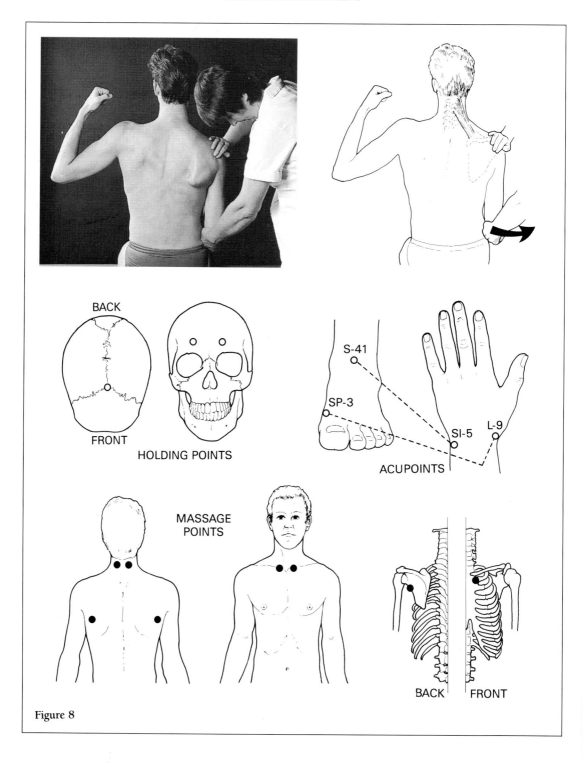

BACK

FRONT

HOLDING POINTS

S-41

SP-3

SI-5

L-9

ACUPOINTS

MASSAGE POINTS

BACK   FRONT

Figure 8

from just behind the inner ankle. Hold it at the same time as L-8 which is on the very end of the arm bone (radius) at the base of the thumb.

Diet

Eye problems, strain, infection, and blurred vision or ear infections and hearing problems can affect and be affected by the upper trapezius because of its pull on the back of the skull and because it affects the balance (ear, eye and head in relation to the body). Foods rich in vitamins A and B and calcium help.

Sports problems

Upper trapezius is used in all sports that use the shoulder girdle. Particularly when reaching up above

the head, such as when practising blocking at volley-ball or tennis service, handstands, shot putt, boxing and rowing, it can become too tight and spasms occur. Fibres can also be torn when the head is wrenched, causing torticollis. By far the most common problem occurs when the shoulders are raised because of stress, constricting some of the blood supply to the head which causes blurred vision and makes it harder to think clearly, so the body tries harder, tension rises – and it becomes a vicious circle. Trapezius also tightens when the athlete is struggling to breathe and support himself/herself on the hands to help use auxilliary breathing muscles (extra ones not normally used).

Exercise

Weight training, shoulder presses, rowing machine.

Levator scapulae

Description

This muscle is found on the back of the shoulder. It runs from the top inner corner of the shoulder-blade to the edges of the top four neck vertebrae (bones). As its name suggests, it lifts the shoulder-blade and draws it in towards the spine.

How to test

(*See Figure 8*) The seated athlete bends the elbow and pushes it down towards the hip whilst keeping the spine as straight as possible. Pressure is put on the inside of the elbow to pull it away from the body as you hold the top of the shoulder down towards the hip (thus putting the rhomboids, which might otherwise be active, at a disadvantage).

Other muscles to test if levator scapulae is weak: rhomboids, trapezius, teres major and minor, latissimus dorsi, neck muscles, pectoralis major clavicular.

HELP
Massage points

1 Top edge of the breastbone just under the collar-bone.
2 Either side of the spine at the back of the base of the neck where the largest vertebra sticks out most.
3 About half-way along the outer edge of the shoulder-blade (in the middle of the teres minor muscle).

Points to hold

1 Frontal eminences – the bumps either side on the forehead above the centre of each eye, half-way up to the hairline.
2 Bregma, the spot just back from the centre top of the head, where the frontal and two parietal (side) bones of the skull join.
3 Acupoints L-9 and Sp-3. L9 is at the base of the thumb on the outside of the wrist crease. Sp-3 is on the heel side of the big joint at the base of the big toe. Hold them together. S-41 and SI-5. S-41 is on the top of the foot in the centre of the ankle

crease. Hold it at the same time as SI-5, which is on the little finger side of the edge of the wrist at the end of the arm bone.

Diet

This muscle will become weak if there is stress or hydrochloric acid disturbance in the stomach causing dyspepsia. Eating tripe, rare meat, chewing food especially well and avoiding sugar and sweet things – particularly immediately before meals – will help. The calming Vitamin B group is good for this as it helps handle stress.

Sports problems

This muscle is used in volley-ball, racket sports, rifle shooting, wind-surfing, rowing and archery. It reacts badly to stress and thus can put uneven pressure on the back of the head, causing headaches, or can twist the neck and generally upset the balance. Together with upper trapezius and SCM it is the cause of many a stiff neck or wry neck. When it is very weak, the athlete will be unable to bring the shoulder-blade in towards the spine without raising the whole shoulder because upper trapezius takes over.

Exercise

Dips and general neck exercises.

Weights – seated and vertical rowing and latissimus dorsi pulls.

MUSCLES OF THE SHOULDER GIRDLE

Subscapularis

Description

The name of this muscle means 'under the shoulder-blade' and that is exactly where you would find it if it were possible to feel under the shoulder-blade – the nearest you can get is to feel the lower inner edge of the shoulder-blade where it is attached. The other end is attached to the top front of the upper arm bone just below the shoulder. Its action is to pull the head of the arm bone in and down when the arm is raised and allows the shoulder-blade to glide over the rib cage.

How to test

(*See Figure 9*)

Test position 1
The athlete sits, raises the arm 90° out to the side and the elbow is bent at 90° so that the forearm hangs down. Stabilize the elbow and push against the wrist to twist the arm forward and up.

Test position 2
The athlete lies face down with the arm out to the side at 90° and hanging off the edge of the table at the elbow. Stabilize the elbow and push the wrist away from the feet. Prevent the elbow from bending more than 90°, pulling in or pulling out.

Other muscles to test if subscapularis is weak: teres major, pectoralis major clavicular and sternal, latissimus dorsi, supraspinatus, abdominals, quadriceps, psoas.

HELP
Massage points

1 Between the second and third rib next to the breastbone.
2 Between the second and third ribs either side of the spine.

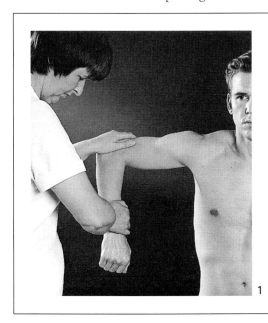
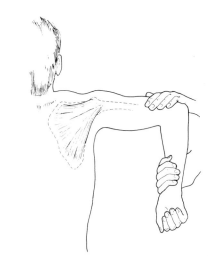

Figure 9

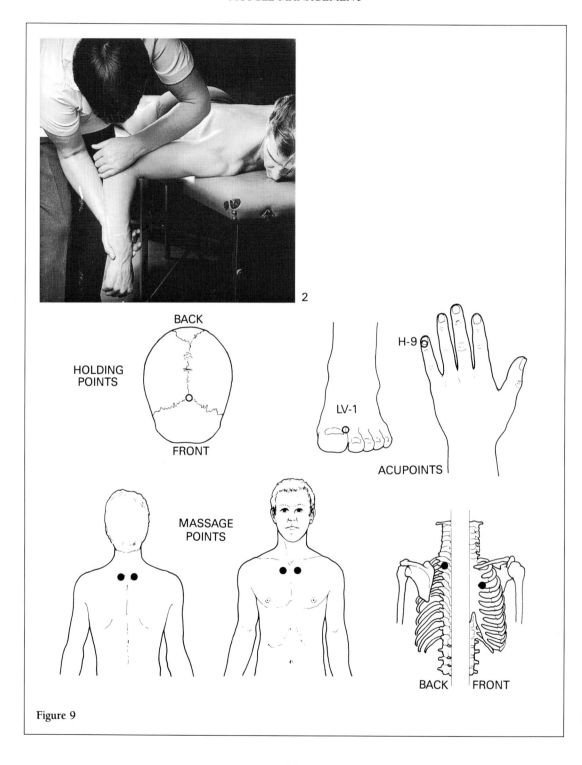

2

HOLDING
POINTS

BACK

FRONT

H-9

LV-1

ACUPOINTS

MASSAGE
POINTS

BACK   FRONT

Figure 9

Points to hold

1 The bregma – the spot just back from the centre top of the head, where the frontal and two parietal (side) bones of the skull join.
2 Acupoints LV-1 and H-9. LV-1 is found on the inside of the nail bed of the big toe. Hold it at the same time as H-9, which is on the nail bed of the little finger.

Diet

The diet to help this muscle should contain sources of calcium, vitamins E and B.

Sports problems

This muscle is one of the four stabilizers of the shoulder joint, holding the upper arm into the socket of the shoulder joint which is very shallow. It is therefore vital to keep it and the joint strong to prevent dislocation in sports where the arms are pulled out by centrifugal force – as in racket sports and gymnastics, field and track events especially throwing. A weak subscapularis will cause chest pains or tightness, shoulder problems and arm pain, palpitations, dizziness and bleeding gums.

Exercise

Rope climbing, chinning, dips on parallel bars.
  Weight training – chest exercises.

Infraspinatus

Description

This muscle is found on the shoulder-blade beneath the horizontal ridge. Like subscapularis it is part of the rotator cuff – four muscles that hold the arm into the shoulder joint. Its action is more or less opposite to subscapularis. Very often it shares a common tendon with teres minor and rotates the arm outwards and backwards with teres minor, being more active when the upper arm is raised above horizontal.

How to test

(*See Figure 10*) The athlete sits with the arm raised to 90° to the outside, the elbow bent 90° to point the forearm vertically. Pressure is put on the back of the wrist to rotate the arm forward and down towards the feet (and even behind). If the shoulder-blade moves, do the same test but with the athlete lying down. The athlete's body weight will help to stabilize the shoulder-blade. Watch for any attempt to flex or extend the arm out of position.

Other muscles to test if infraspinatus is weak: teres minor, supraspinatus, trapezius (upper and middle), rhomboids.

HELP

Massage points

1 Between the fifth and sixth ribs near the breast-bone on the right chest wall.
2 Just above the lowest rib either side of the spine.
3 On the back, either side of the spine between the second and third ribs.

Points to hold

1 The angle of Louis – the ridge about three fingers down from the top of the breastbone.
2 Acupoints GB-41 and T-3. GB-41 is on the top of the foot where the bones extending back from the fourth and fifth toes join (this is about half-way between the base of the toes and the ankle). Hold this point at the same time as T-3, which is in a similar position on the back of the hand.

Diet

This muscle seems to indicate thymus and thyroid function and therefore responds to foods high in natural iodine such as seaweed and seafood gener-

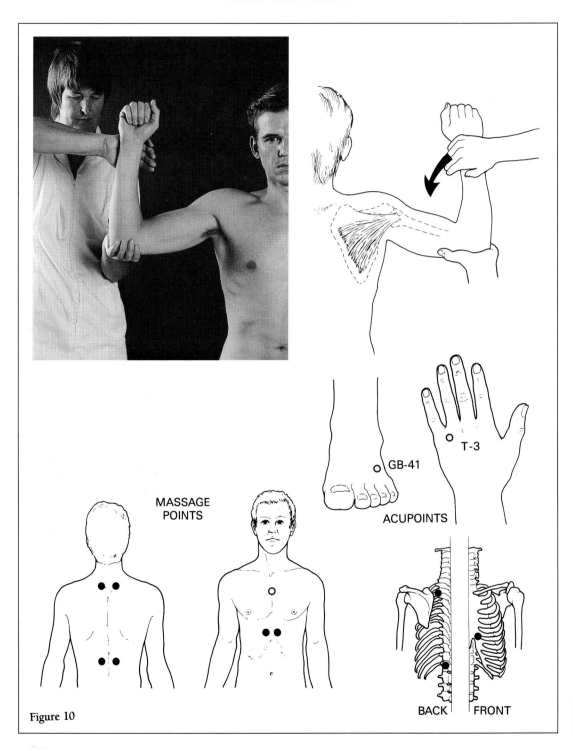

MASSAGE POINTS

ACUPOINTS

GB-41

T-3

BACK   FRONT

Figure 10

ally. Symptoms can be of digestive disturbance, weight change and unwarranted or uncontrolled crying. The athlete may alos have difficulty losing weight even though dieting. The athlete may feel tired or find it very hard to get out of bed in the morning. The sluggishness will often be accompanied by cold or chapped hands and feet and getting out of breath or sweating a lot with comparatively little exertion. If high doses of Vitamin A have been taken for other reasons and some of these symptoms are apparent, look and see if perhaps a good thing has been overdone, and avoid cheese, bananas and oats.

Sports problems

Because it is a rotator cuff muscle, the comments given under teres minor and subscapularis apply here also. A weak infraspinatus leads to elbow, wrist and shoulder difficulties.

Exercise

Jumping jacks, push-ups, skipping, swimming,.
  Weights - dumb-bells and vertical rowing.

Supraspinatus

Description

This muscle joins the upper half of the shoulder-blade to the upper arm and so lifts the arm out sideways as a help to the stronger deltoid muscles. Its main function could be said to be to hold the very top of the arm bone into the socket and pull more horizontally than the deltoid group.

How to test

(*See Figure 11*) The athlete sits or stands and turns the head away from the side being tested to inactivate the upper trapezius as much as possible. The arm is taken out to the side and forward about 15° (beyond 20° the deltoids take over), palm in and thumb forward. Pressure is put on the back of the wrist to push the arm back to the centre of the groin. Watch that the shoulder is not raised by putting a finger on top of the bones at the outer end of the shoulder – however, too far in and you are touching the muscle itself. Watch, too, that the athlete does not try to twist the spine to the side and try and use the trapezius muscle instead. Compare tests of deltoid and supra-spinatus, as deltoid is always a little active in this test.

Other muscles to test if supraspinatus is weak: upper trapezius, deltoid, pectoralis major sternal and clavicular.

HELP
Massage points

1 From the dip just inside the shoulder joint on the front of the body (under the outer end of the collar bone) down along the side of the chest for about 4″ (10 cm).
2 As high as you can right up under the skull at the top of the neck, either side of the spine.

Points to hold

1 Frontal eminence and bregma together. Frontal eminences are on the forehead half-way between the centre of the eyebrows and hairline. The bregma is the spot just back from the centre top of the head, where the frontal and two parietal (side) bones of the skull join.
2 There are no acupoints for this muscle charted yet.

Diet

Foods high in lecithin, such as soya beans, may be helpful. Make sure the athlete stays away from rich fatty foods, alcohol, tobacco, caffeine, high sugar content in foods, and medications containing epine-phrine and cortisol unless prescribed by the doctor.

Sports problems

Supraspinatus is used in golf, racket sports and

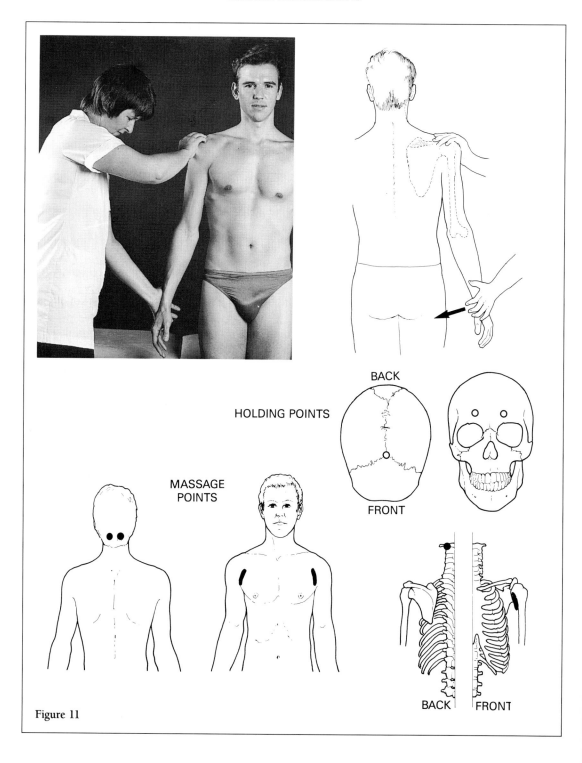

BACK

HOLDING POINTS

FRONT

MASSAGE
POINTS

Figure 11

BACK   FRONT

baseball. Weakness to this muscle can also be caused by poor breathing, whiplash injuries and injury and trauma to the head, long dental procedures, wearing too tight helmets or practising too many 'headers' as in football. It can also be affected by severe emotional upset, anxiety or mental fatigue. Weakness will cause shoulder problems.

Exercise

Dips, dumb-bell or bar-bell extensions above the head. People who are weekend athletes and spend their working life doing desk work, thinking hard or driving many miles can suffer from 'brain fag' which will also weaken supraspinatus. It is well known that you need a rest after a long drive for this reason before playing in a golf match. Supraspinatus is used in golf particularly in the back swing, which sets up the whole shot, whether it be drive or putter. Golf is also known to be particularly testing in self-control and emotional stress if you take the game seriously at all.

Rhomboids

Description

These muscles are short and powerful and so close together they often help each other. They join the inner edge of the shoulder-blade to the spine in the upper back. They draw the shoulder-blades together.

How to test

(*See Figure 12*)   These muscles are rarely found weak as they help each other and are also helped by levator scapulae. The athlete sits or lies, bends the elbow so that the hand is on the front of the shoulder (*not* on the chest wall). The other arm is raised to inactivate the other rhomboids. Pressure is put on the inside of the upper arm to pull it away from the body to the side. Watch that the shoulders are level. The shoulder may lift slightly as you test. If it does not, then the middle trapezius is doing the work. If the rhomboid is weak, then the shoulder blade will pull away from the spine as you test.

Other muscles to test if rhomboids are weak: the other rhomboid, upper trapezius, levator scapulae, anterior serratus, anterior deltoid, latissimus dorsi, pectoralis major sternal.

HELP
Massage Points

1   Between the fifth and sixth ribs on the left of the chest wall (one rib space down from the nipple).
2   Between the fifth and sixth ribs on the left side and next to the spine. Authorities vary as to whether these points are on the right or left sides of the body – if both sides are tender, do both.

Points to hold

1   Bregma – the spot just back from the centre top of the head, where the frontal and two parietal (side) bones of the skull join.
2   Frontal eminences – on either side of the fore-head, between the middle of the eyebrow and the hairline.
3   Acupoints LV-8 and K-10. LV-8 is found in-between the lower inner end of the thigh bone and the hamstring tendon near the inner-knee crease. K-10 is almost next-door, at the innermost end of the knee crease when the knee is bent.

Diet

The association of this muscle is with the liver and stomach, so avoid rich fatty and fried foods, all forms of caffeine and fizzy drinks. Eat foods rich in Vitamin A.

Sports problems

These muscles are particularly used in gymnastics on pommel, rings and parallel bars, mainly to fix the position of the upper body with the arms. They are used in volley-ball and rowing, archery and wind-surfing.

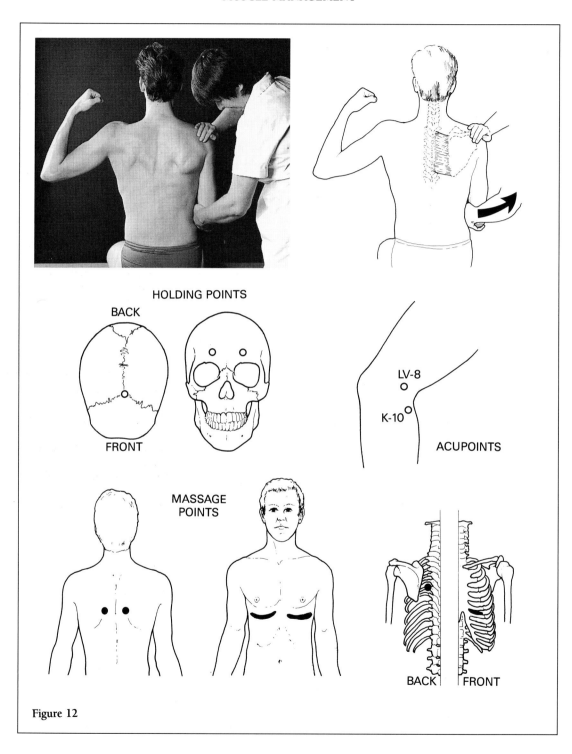

HOLDING POINTS

BACK

FRONT

LV-8

K-10

ACUPOINTS

MASSAGE POINTS

BACK FRONT

Figure 12

They are also used in swimming, especially in breaststroke. Most problems occur when there is one-sided use as in racket sports, rifle shooting, javelin and other throwing sports which strengthen all the arm and shoulder muscles on one side, and then pull several of the upper thoracic vertebrae between the shoulder-blades across to that side, making rhomboids flaccid on one side and tense on the other side.

Exercise

Exercise with weights – seated and vertical rowing, lateral pulls. Latissimus dorsi pulls.

Deltoids (anterior, middle and posterior)

Description

The deltoids are the group of muscles that join the upper arm to the shoulder, spreading round the point of the shoulder like epaulettes. They are extremely strong and, because they are wrapped around the arm and shoulder, they lift the arm forward (anterior division), sideways (middle division), and backwards (posterior division). This means that the front and back divisions can work against each other.

How to test

(*See Figure 13*)   The athlete sits or stands, raises the arms out 90° to the side and bends the elbow 90° so the forearm is horizontal. Watch that there is no arm rotation or body shift away to avoid the test.

(a) *Anterior deltoid*
Support the back and top of the shoulder as you pull the inside of the elbow backwards and downwards. Make sure the shoulder-blade is not allowed to rise up.

(b) *Middle deltoid*
Support the shoulder and then push the test elbow down and in to the side of the body.

(c) *Posterior deltoid*
Support the front of the shoulder to stop the body twisting and tipping sideways. Press on the back of the elbow forward, down and into the body.

Other Muscles to test if the deltoids are weak: the other deltoid divisions, coracobrachialis, infraspinatus, teres major, supraspinatus, pectoralis major clavicular and sternal.

HELP
Massage points

1 Between the third, fourth and fifth ribs either side of the breastbone.
2 Between the third, fourth and fifth thoracic vertebrae (also third, fourth and fifth rib) in-between the shoulder-blades, either side of the spine.

Points to hold

1 Bregma – the spot just back from the centre top of the head, where the frontal and parietal (side) bones of the skull join.
2 Acupoints B-66 and GB-43. B-66 is on the outside of the foot at the base of the little toe. Hold it at the same time as GB-43, which is next-door at the base of the fourth toe.
3 Acupoints SP-3 and L-9. SP-3 is on the heel side of the big joint at the base of the big toe (on the side of the foot). Hold it at the same time as L-9, which is at the base of the thumb on the outside of the wrist crease.

Diet

Anterior deltoid reacts badly to over-rich foods and body toxicity – the sort of problem that can give you a bad headache (like lifting too many heavy pint beer mugs!). Middle and posterior deltoids react badly to breathing congestion, 'flu and smoking. All divisions of the deltoids are helped by Vitamins A and C.

Sports problems

Weakness in anterior deltoid is indicated when the

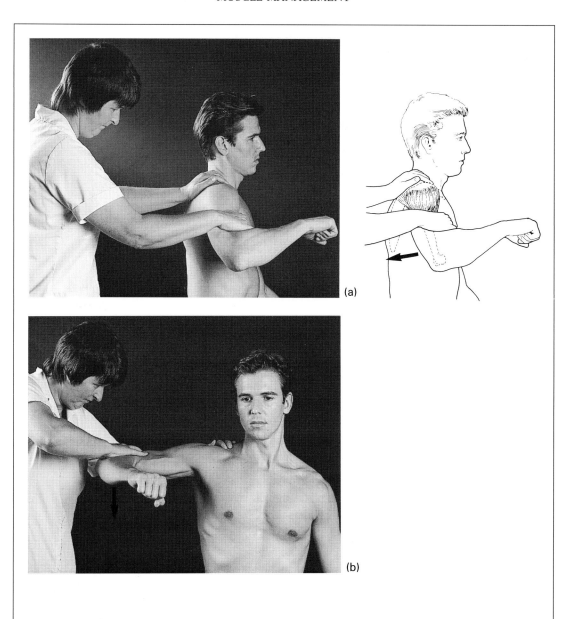

(a)

(b)

Figure 13

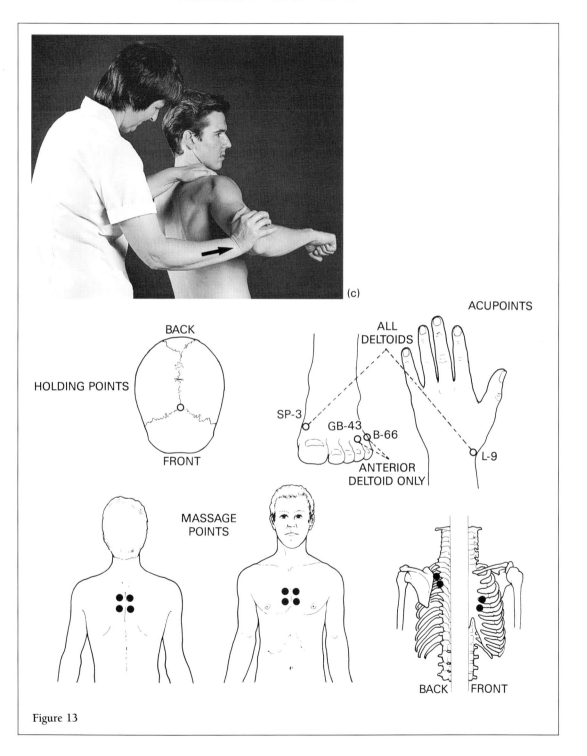

(c)

ACUPOINTS

ALL DELTOIDS

HOLDING POINTS

BACK

FRONT

SP-3

GB-43 B-66

ANTERIOR DELTOID ONLY

L-9

MASSAGE POINTS

BACK   FRONT

Figure 13

43

athlete can't put his or her hands in their back pocket. Middle deltoid is involved in swinging the arm in walking and it is also helping the posterior division. Another function is lifting the arms away from the body slightly to clear the trunk. In general, however, deltoids work hardest when the arm is lifted more than 90° and weakness can cause shoulder, collar-bone and rib problems. Posterior deltoid is most involved in the co-ordination of swinging the arms in the gait mechanism that balances the body as you walk (see Chapter 6). The conclusion from the above is that deltoids are involved in much more than just lifting the arm and preparing for such things as tennis smash shots, bowling, cricket, balancing upside-down on rings, javelin and wind-surfing but also in the general balance and co-ordination of the top versus the bottom of the body.

In looking at the parts, don't forget the whole. When a muscle is put out of action by, say, a fall onto the shoulder it will upset much more than just that muscle. Co-ordination goes, too. If there are continuous problems with deltoids, check Gaits in Chapter 6.

Exercise

Weights – vertical rowing, bench and shoulder press.

Pectoralis minor

Description

This muscle runs from the third, fourth and fifth ribs on the chest to the outer end of the shoulder-blade just above the shoulder joint, so it draws the ribs and shoulders together. It is important in stabilizing the front of the shoulder. It is also one of the extra breathing muscles that can be used to raise the ribs when there is a problem with the normal breathing muscles, or in forced inspiration.

How to test

(*See Figure 14*)   The athlete lies on his or her back and raises the shoulder forward and off the table and downward towards the hip (together with the rest of the arm so as to prevent it from supporting the shoulders). Pressure is then put on the front of the shoulder to push it back down to the table. Make sure your direction of push comes as though from the opposite hip.

Other muscles to test if pectoralis minor is weak: pectoralis major clavicular and sternal.

HELP
Massage points

1 At the lower end of the breastbone where the lowest ribs join, just above the softer xiphoid bone which hangs down in the upturned 'V' between the ribs.
2 There are none on the back.

Points to hold

1 On the temple about 1″ (1.5 cm) to the side of the outer corner of the eye.
2 Acupoints are presently under research.

Diet

Foods rich in Vitamin B complex.

Since this muscle controls the ribs that directly cover the main drainage of lymph back into the blood, they therefore have an effect on the whole lymph drainage and immune system of the body, especially if the athlete spends a lot of time with his/her head below the feet.

Sports problems

This muscle is far more likely to be too tense than weak, causing round shoulders, limiting the breathing and causing poor lymph drainage. A sure sign is if you always wake with your hands above your head. Such a position as this will clear the above problem as long as they remain there. However, no one wants to have their hands raised all day! You can deal with

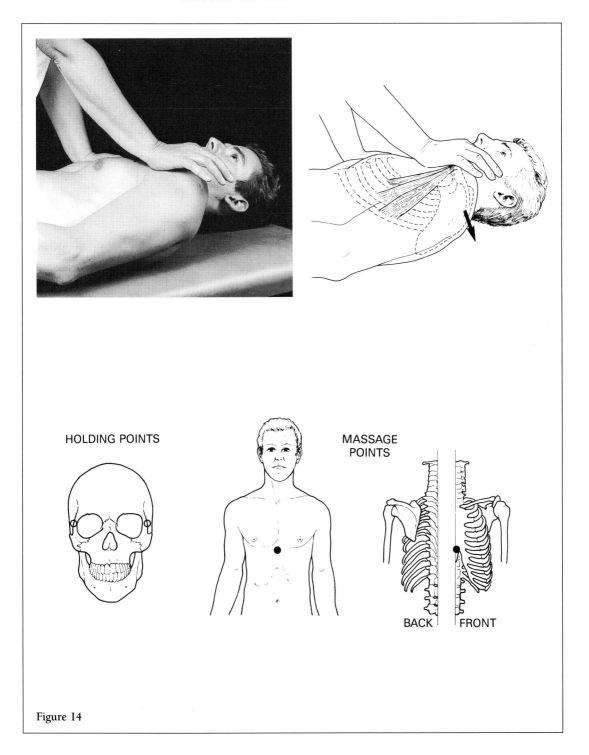

HOLDING POINTS

MASSAGE POINTS

BACK | FRONT

Figure 14

this problem by firmly but gently stretching the three strands of the muscle as it goes from the outer corner of the shoulder to the third, fourth and fifth ribs (using a little talc or oil to stop skin burn).

Teres minor

Description

This muscle runs from half-way up the outer side of the back of the shoulder-blade to the back of the arm, so it draws the arm in and twists the upper arm outward (opposite to teres major). It is often joined to infraspinatus and has a rather similar action. The major difference is that to test teres minor the arm is held in to the body, whereas infraspinatus is held 90° away from the body when testing. Teres minor also directly opposes subscapularis and is one of the 'rotator cuff' muscles that holds the upper arm into the shoulder joint.

How to test

(*See Figure 15*) The athlete sits with the elbow bent 90°, palm turning in and with the upper arm held in to the side. Support and stabilize the elbow and push the back of the forearm in across the chest. Be sure that the athlete is not twisting or moving the upper arm or body to use other muscles such as triceps or biceps.

Other muscles to test if teres minor is weak: infraspinatus, trapezius and rhomboids (if these are weak, teres minor will appear weak – indicated by shoulder blade movement which should not happen).

HELP
Massage points

1 Between the second and third ribs, immediately either side of the breastbone.
2 Between the second and third ribs where they join the second and third thoracic vertebrae at the top of the back, level with the top of the shoulder-blade.

Pectoralis minor is used particularly in climbing and gymnastics.

Exercise

Weights – dipping and latissimus dorsi pulls.

Points to hold

1 Just in the hairline half-way between the corner of the eye and where the top of the ear joins the head.
2 At the junction of the collar-bones and breastbone.
3 Acupoints GB-41 and T-3. GB-41 is found on the top of the foot half-way between the base of the fourth toe and the ankle. Hold it at the same time as T-3, which is on the back of the hand half-way between the base of the ring finger and the wrist on the little finger side of the bone.

Diet

This muscle can be an indicator of thyroid function and therefore responds to organic iodine which is found in seaweed and seafood. Another indicator of malfunction would be excessive or unreasonable crying when stressed or overwrought.

Sports problems

If teres minor is weak it is sometimes difficult for the athlete to raise the arm as the muscle is working out of synchronization with the deltoids. (See 'Reactive muscles' in Chapter 6 for this.) As a 'rotator cuff' muscle it is important to check its strength after any shoulder injury or during rehabilitation.

This muscle is particularly used in swimming and backhand in racket sports. Weakness can cause elbow and wrist problems and general shoulder-joint weakness.

Exercise

Jumping jacks, push-ups, skipping and swimming.
    Weights – dumb-bells and vertical rowing.

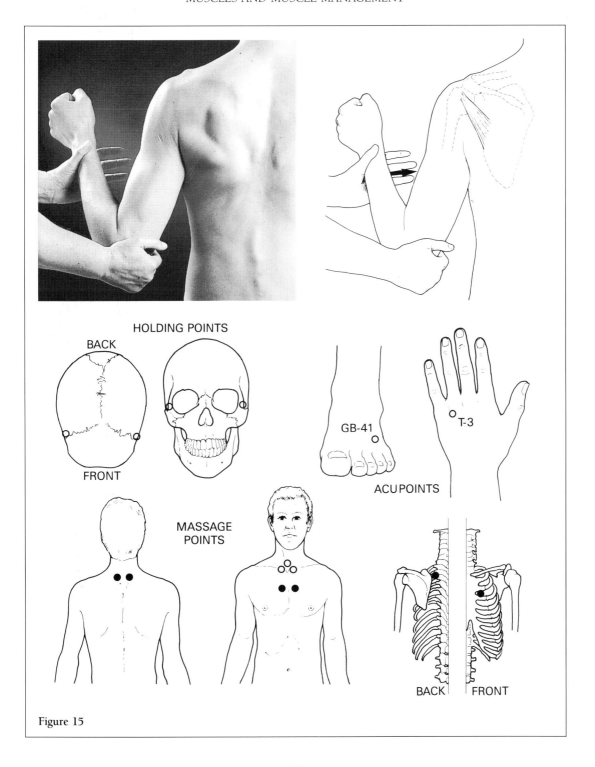

Figure 15

47

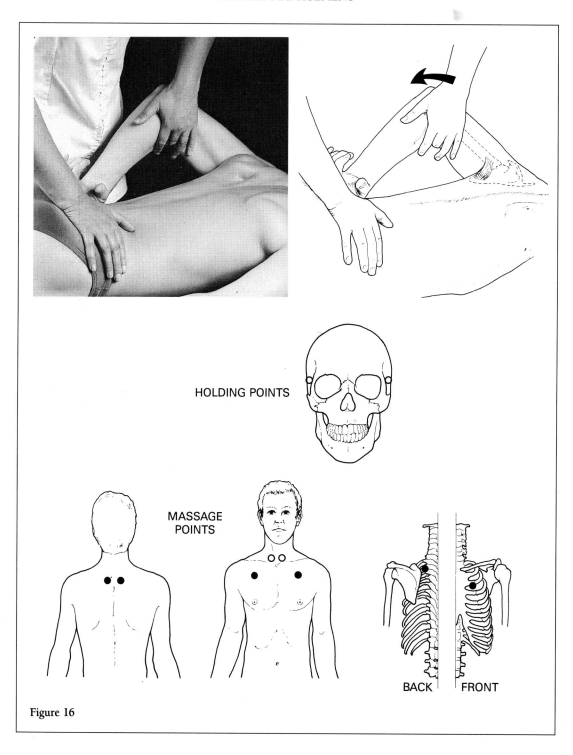

HOLDING POINTS

MASSAGE
POINTS

BACK | FRONT

Figure 16

Teres major

Description

This muscle runs from the bottom corner of the shoulder-blade to the top front of the upper arm so it draws the arm in towards the body, turning it inwards, but at the same time pulls it back behind the body to be nearer the shoulder-blade. The athlete uses it particularly when pushing his or her hands up behind their back – as though to undo a bra-strap.

How to test

(*See Figure 16*) The best test position is with the athlete lying face down. The arm is bent back so that the back of the fist is resting on the back of the hips. (Stabilize the opposite shoulder or hip to prevent body rock if necessary.) Push the elbow of the bent arm out to the side and down. Be careful not to push too hard as you are in a position of great relative strength compared with the athlete. The shoulder-blade should not move if held properly by trapezius or rhomboids.

Other muscles to test if teres major is weak: trapezius (especially middle division), rhomboids.

HELP

Massage points

1 One rib space down from the collar-bone (between the second and third ribs) on a line straight up from the nipple and third out from the breastbone.
2 Either side of the spine near the top of the back, between the second and third ribs where they join the second and third thoracic vertebrae.

Coracobrachialis

Description

This muscle works together with the anterior

Points to hold

1 Half-way between the corner of the eye and where the top of the ear joins the head.
2 One inch (2.5 cm) below the front of the neck where the collar-bones meet the breastbone.
3 Acupoints are currently being researched.

Diet

When this muscle is weak there may be an acid/alkaline imbalance in the body and/or warts on the soles of the feet. If the athlete perspires enormously then kelp, which is found in seaweed, will help. Seafoods, particularly, but also eggs, dairy products and meat, are helpful sources of protein. If food seems tasteless, then, rather than adding condiments, take zinc and trace minerals. Men in particular have a need for zinc.

Sports problems

The inward arm rotation aspect of this muscle is not used much except against resistance. Generally it is used more to hold the arm backwards – together with posterior deltoid – in such positions as rowing, cross-country skiing, or when the arm is back in the crawl stroke in swimming or in the flying stage of ski-jumping or sleighing to improve the aerodynamics by decreasing wind resistance and increasing balance. Teres major is very important in problems such as 'frozen shoulder' and weakness will also cause rib problems, cramps and warts on the feet.

Exercise

Chinning, rope climbing, dips on parallel bars.
   Weights – seated rowing and latissimus dorsi pulls.

division of the deltoids. It runs from inside the top outer edge of the shoulder-blade to the inside of upper arm, so it draws the arm up and in.

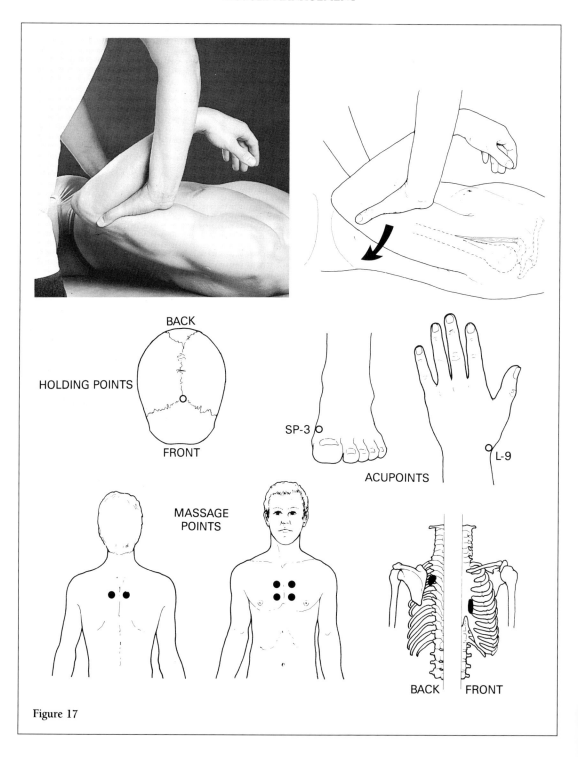

BACK

HOLDING POINTS

FRONT

SP-3

ACUPOINTS

L-9

MASSAGE POINTS

BACK FRONT

Figure 17

How to test

(*See Figure 17*) With the athlete sitting or lying on his or her back, the elbow is bent as far as possible (to reduce the action of biceps). The palm faces towards the shoulder as the arm is raised 45° up and forward and turned slightly outward. If the athlete is sitting, support the outer back of the shoulder.

Another test of coracobrachialis is to bring the athlete's straight arm forward 45° with palm facing upwards. Pressure is put on the lower arm to push it back to the side of the body. The hand position inhibits anterior deltoid.

Other muscles to test if coracobrachialis is weak: deltoids, anterior serratus, diaphragm, pectoralis major, biceps.

HELP
Massage points

1 Between the third and fourth ribs next to the breastbone.
2 Between the fourth and fifth ribs either side of the spine (between the shoulder-blades).

Points to hold

1 Bregma – the spot just back from the centre top of the head, where the frontal and parietal (side) bones of the skull join.

2 Acupoints SP-3 and L-9. SP-3 is the heel side of the large joint at the base of the big toe on the side of the foot. Hold it at the same time as L-9, which is at the base of the thumb on the end of the wrist crease.

Diet

This muscle weakness may accompany chronic coughs and other lung problems. Take plenty of Vitamin C.

Sports problems

This muscle is used in rowing, tug-of-war, boxing and archery. A sign of coracobrachialis weakness is an inability to put the hand behind the head or difficulty combing the hair, also in straightening the arm when it is held over the head. The arms feel weak and tired. It is also used in eating and the athlete will complain that their arm gets tired when they eat! It is therefore an essential muscle in all overhead sports or where protection of the head by the hands is required. A weak coracobrachialis may also lead to insomnia and chronic cough which is more usually associated with pre-match nerves or asthma.

Exercise

Weights – biceps curls, latissimus dorsi pulls and chinning.

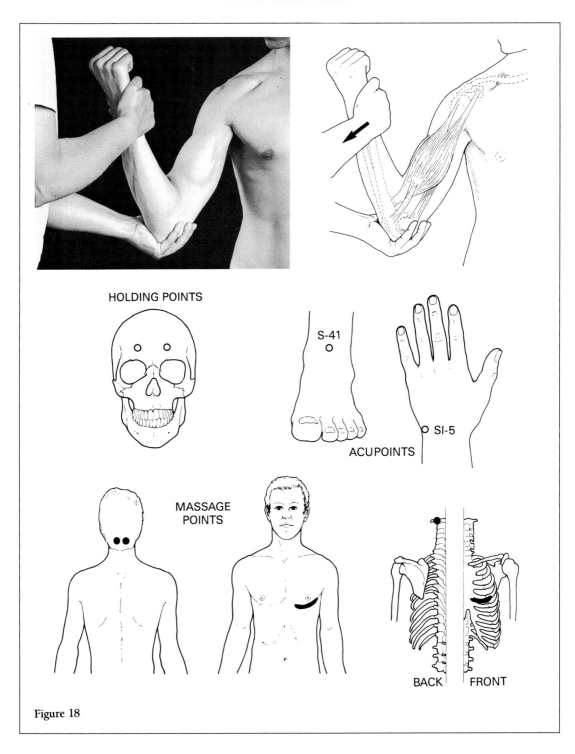

HOLDING POINTS

S-41

SI-5

ACUPOINTS

MASSAGE POINTS

BACK   FRONT

Figure 18

ARM, WRIST AND HAND MUSCLES

Biceps brachii and brachialis

Description

These muscles are both found on the front of the upper arm and have a similar action, so are considered here together. They both bend the elbow. The biceps actually crosses two joints (shoulder and elbow) because it is attached twice at one end to the shoulder-blade and at the other end to the radius (the bone on the thumb side of the forearm) whereas brachialis runs from the humerus (upper arm bone) to the ulna (the bone on the little finger side of the forearm). Although not terribly well arranged mechanically for lifting, they are extra strong to make up for any inefficiency.

How to test

(*See Figure 18*)   The athlete sits and bends the arm not quite to a right angle (75°) (because the muscles are so strong). The palm faces towards the shoulder (to put brachioradialis at a disadvantage). The elbow is supported whilst pressure is put on the inside of the wrist to straighten the arm.

Other muscles to test if biceps brachii and brachialis are weak: brachioradialis, rhomboids, neck flexors, teres major and minor, pectoralis major clavicular, latissimus dorsi.

HELP

Massage points

1 Between the fourth and fifth ribs, 3″ (8 cm) either side of the breastbone.
2 Either side of the very top of the spine where it meets the skull.

Points to hold

1 Frontal eminences – half-way between the centre of each eyebrow and the hairline, either side of the forehead.
2 Acupoints S-41 and SI-5. S-41 is on the top of the foot in the centre of the ankle crease. Hold it together with SI-5, which is on the little finger side of the wrist at the end of the arm bone.

Diet

This muscle is associated with stomach disorders and gluten sensitivity, so go carefully in what you eat. Chew everything very well and avoid all allergens – especially food containing white sugars and white flour.

Sports problems

These muscles work when you 'chin' a high beam and play forehand or top-spin backhand in racket sports. It is also used in baseball, gymnastics, boxing, swimming, wrestling and javelin (when taking the arm back). Over-practising one particular technique can overtire these muscles and/or give you shoulder problems. If you find this happening, stop, work on the help points and go through your techniques mentally (see 'Visualization' in Chapter 7).

Exercise

Forearm flexions with weights, push-ups, chinning.
   Weight – biceps curls, latissimus dorsi pulls.

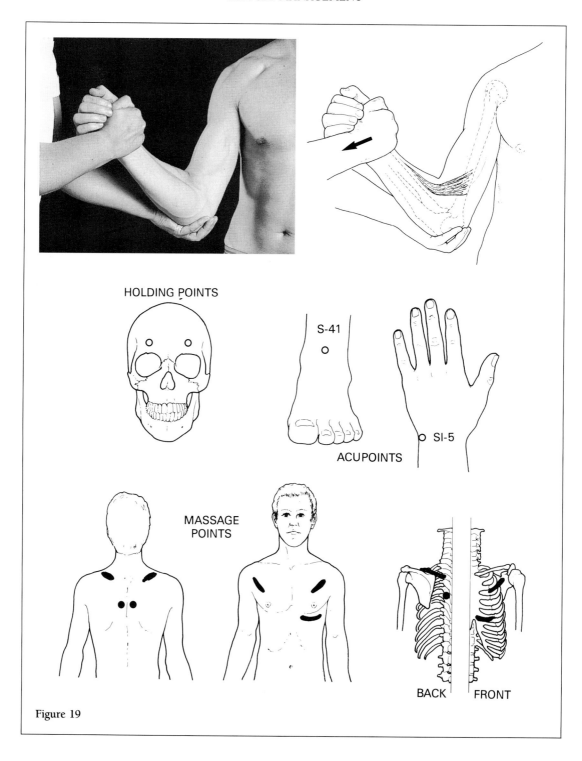

HOLDING POINTS

S-41

SI-5

ACUPOINTS

MASSAGE
POINTS

BACK   FRONT

Figure 19

Brachioradialis

Description

This muscle flexes (bends) the elbow, assisting biceps brachii and brachialis, but when the arm is turned so that the palm faces in and down, it is really a strength muscle, only coming into play when you are lifting weights more than 4 lbs (2 kg). There appears to be more strength in the elbows when the palm is facing in, (using biceps brachii and brachialis) than when the palm is facing down. However, brachioradialis is particularly active in quick bursts of activity.

How to test

(*See Figure 19*)   The athlete sits or lies and bends the elbow 75°. The hand is turned so the palm faces in towards the body (thumb up). Stabilize the elbow or let it rest on a firm (but not uncomfortably hard) surface. Pressure is put upon the forearm to straighten the arm. Watch for twisting the hand round – the athlete will be trying to use biceps brachii instead.

Other muscles to test if brachioradialis is weak: biceps brachii and brachialis, rhomboids, neck flexors, teres major and minor, latissimus dorsi, pectoralis major clavicular.

HELP
Massage points

1 Between the fifth and sixth ribs, the breadth of the left side of the chest wall.
2 Over the entire area of pectoralis muscles, especially pectoralis minor (see pages 44-6).
3 Between the fifth and sixth thoracic vertebrae either side of the spine - level with the middle of the shoulder-blades.
4 The top edge of the shoulder-blade (above the ridge).

Points to hold

1 Frontal eminences – the points on either side of the forehead half-way between the centre of the eyebrow and the hairline.
2 Acupoints - as for biceps brachii (see page 53).

Diet

As for biceps brachii.

Sports problems

Similar to biceps brachii, but weak brachioradialis also causes difficulty in putting the bent arms up behind the back.
  This muscle is used in rowing, climbing, canoeing, basketball and boxing.

Exercise

Weights - biceps curls, latissimus dorsi pulls, chinning.

Triceps brachii and anconeus

Description

These muscles on the back of the arm work together to straighten the arm. Triceps has three heads, two on the upper arm and one on the shoulder-blade (which also helps to pull the upper arm in). Anconeus is much shorter and tucked in on the outer edge, just above the elbow, and both muscles go across the elbow joint and attach onto the forearm bones.

How to test

(*See Figure 20*)   These muscles are tested together as their action is so similar. The athlete is seated, the arm

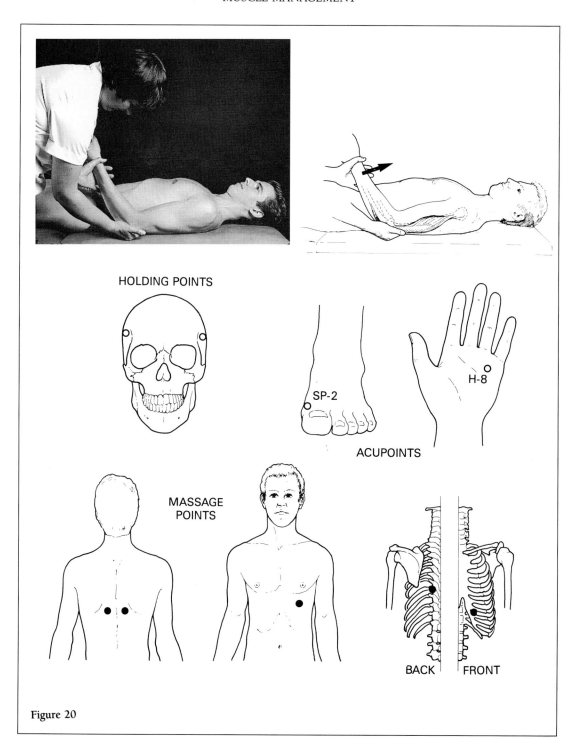

HOLDING POINTS

SP-2

H-8

ACUPOINTS

MASSAGE
POINTS

BACK   FRONT

Figure 20

is extended at 45° and bent at 45° at the elbow. The front of the upper arm is stabilized whilst pressure is put on the back of the wrist to bend the elbow further. If testing a child, have the arm almost straight.

Other muscles to test if triceps is weak: levator scapulae, rhomboids and latissimus dorsi.

HELP
Massage points

1 Between the seventh and eighth ribs near the cartilage on the left.
2 On the back, either side of the spine at the seventh–eighth thoracic vertebrae – about level with the bottom of the shoulder-blades.

Points to hold

1 On the parietal bone just above and behind the ear.
2 Acupoints SP-2 and H-8. SP-2 is found on the nail end of the big joint at the base of the big toe on the side of the foot. Hold it at the same time as H-8, which is on the palm of the hand on the first crease just below the base of the ring finger.

Diet

Avoid sweets and refined sugars. This muscle is affected in the same way as latissimus dorsi. Eat foods that contain vitamin A.

Sports problems

Triceps is used in volley-ball (pitcher), shot-putt, basketball (shooter). These muscles work opposite the biceps muscle group and so are important in any sport using the arms, providing power in throwing and javelin, also providing balance when bending the arms when doing handstands and hand spring, and control in backhands in racket sports. Pain in the back of the arm can be referred from the neck or the wrist. Weakness of both can cause elbow and shoulder problems and carbohydrate sensitivity. Triceps is also often blamed for 'tennis' and 'golf elbows', but before you think that, make sure latissimus dorsi is strong as elbow pain is often due to overwork of triceps when latissimus dorsi is weak. Do the General Hand Muscle Test (page 65) for good measure, too.

Exercise

Dips on a parallel bar, push-ups, pressing a bar-bell or dumb-bell upward.

Seated rowing, lateral pulls, press-ups, shoulder and bench press.

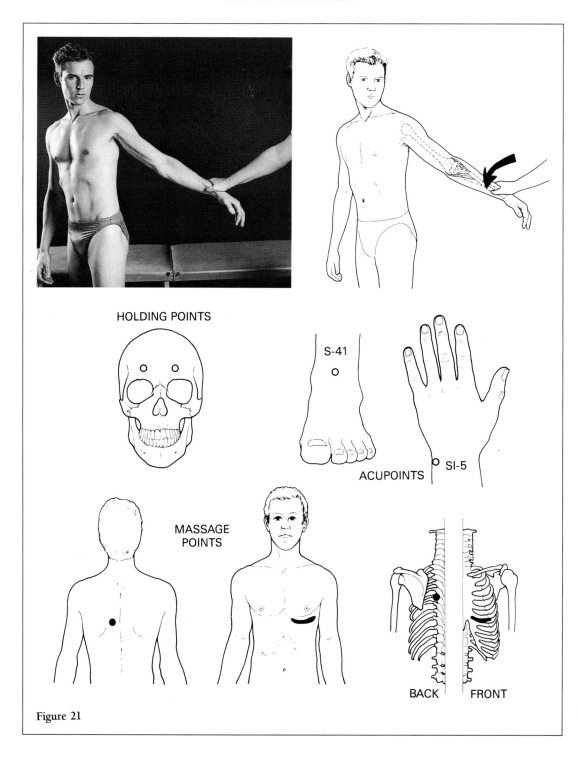

HOLDING POINTS

S-41

ACUPOINTS

SI-5

MASSAGE POINTS

BACK   FRONT

Figure 21

SUPINATORS AND PRONATORS OF THE ARM AND WRIST

Supinator

Description

This muscle turns the forearm from palm down to palm up. It is located at the elbow joint on the outside. – mostly between the radius (large forearm bone) and humerus (upper arm bone), but reaching across the ulna (small forearm bone) as well.

How to test

(*See Figure 21*)   The athlete sits. The arm is extended backwards, palm to the floor. Stabilize the upper arm above the elbow so that it does not twist. With your other hand, grasp the athlete just above the wrist and twist the forearm to face palm outward. You can also test with arm bent and palm up, but here biceps brachii is also very active and can confuse the test. Hold the elbow underneath and twist the wrist in towards the body. In both tests watch that the athlete does not twist the upper arm.

Other muscles to test if supinators are weak: triceps, biceps brachii.

HELP

Massage points

1 Between the fifth and sixth ribs on the left (under the breast) towards the breastbone.
2 Between sixth and seventh thoracic vertebrae on the left of the spine – one rib space above the level of the bottom of the shoulder blades.

Points to hold

1 Frontal eminence – the points either side of the forehead between the centre of the eyebrow and the hairline.
2 Acupoints S-41 and SI-4. See also pronators (page 61).

Diet

Eat extra vitamins B complex and B_2.

Sports problems

Supinator is used especially in backhand racket sports and in water-ski grip.

Exercise

Weights – biceps curls and dumb-bells.

Pronator teres and pronator quadratus

Description

These are both muscles that turn the forearm bones so that the palm faces down towards the feet when the arm is bent or behind you when the arm is straight. Pronator teres is at the elbow and crosses the elbow joint, twisting the two forearm bones against each other. In order to turn the arm as far as possible, both muscles are needed.

How to test

(*See Figure 22*)   The athlete lies on his or her back,

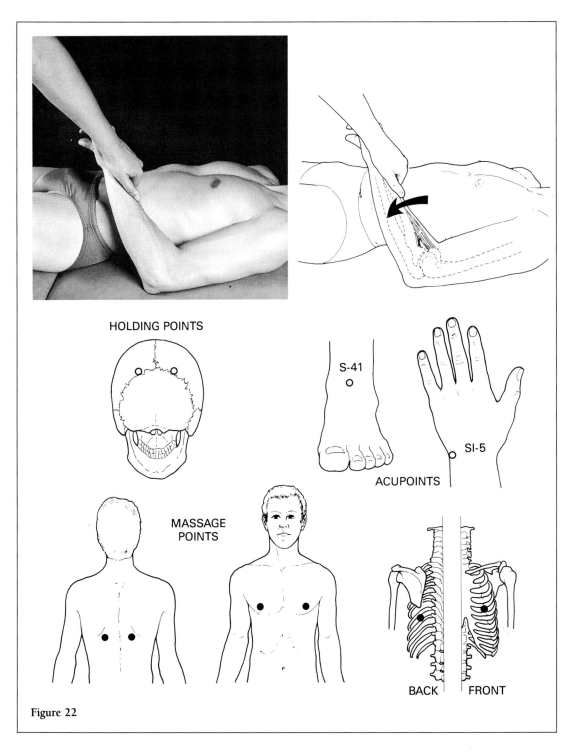

HOLDING POINTS

S-41

SI-5

ACUPOINTS

MASSAGE
POINTS

BACK   FRONT

Figure 22

the elbow is held firmly in to the side of the body and bent 60°. The hand is turned so that the palm faces away from the head. Stabilize the underneath of the elbow (don't wrap your fingers round the inside of the elbow, hold along it instead). Pressure is put on the forearm above the wrist to twist the forearm outwards so that the palm faces towards the head. This tests both pronator muscles together. To differentiate, pronator quadratus works mosty when the elbow is flexed more, placing pronator teres at a disadvantage. Be careful that the force of the twist of your test does not cause pain at the contact point because that will make the test weak whether the muscles are weak or not.

Other muscles to test if pronators are weak: brachioradialis.

HELP

Massage points

1 On the rib cage between fourth and fifth ribs, behind the nipples.
2 Between the eighth and ninth ribs on the back, just below the lowest point of the shoulder-blades.

Points to hold

1 On the back of the head 2½″ (4 cm) diagonally up and out 45° from the centre top of the neck.
2 Acupoints S-41 and SI-5. S-41 is on the top of the foot in the centre of the ankle crease. SI-5 is on the little finger side of the wrist, at the end of the arm bone. Hold them at the same time.

Diet

These muscles can be involved in carpal tunnel syndrome pain and there is an association with stomach function, both of which respond to B vitamins and especially pyridoxine (B_6) and riboflavin (B_2).

Sports problems

The ability to turn the hands is so important in so many sports. Perhaps the most obvious is to put top or back spin on a ball in racket sports.

In daily life weak pronators cause problems with turning doorknobs and picking up a full cup. They are often involved in carpal tunnel syndrome (when the nerve to the thumb and two fingers becomes trapped causing loss of function, pain, or pins and needles). If the supinator muscle is in spasm it is sometimes involved in entrapment of the radial nerve as it passes through the muscle, causing referred pain to the hand and shoulder.

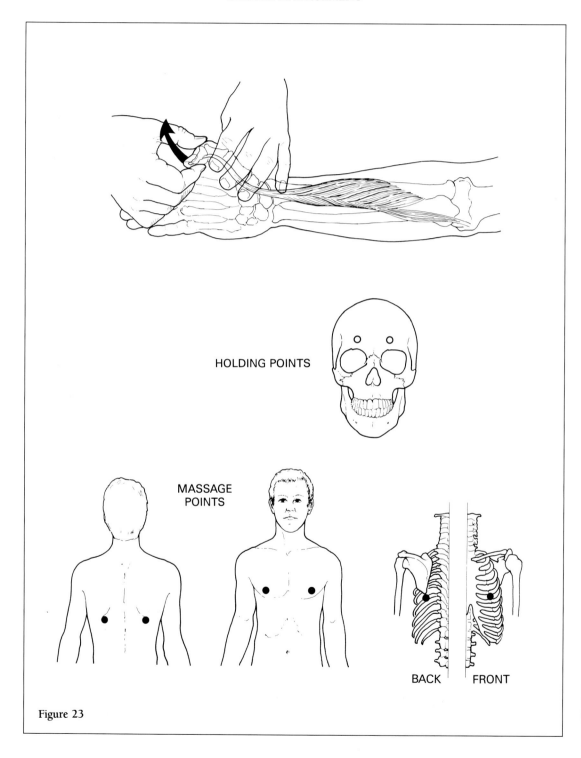

HOLDING POINTS

MASSAGE
POINTS

BACK   FRONT

Figure 23

THE MUSCLES OF THE HAND

Description

Surprisingly, many of the muscles that bend and stretch the fingers are not on the hand at all but on the forearm, with tendons going across the wrist joint to the fingers. I have confined myself to describing a few of the largest and simplest muscles, including some on the hand itself.

Perhaps the most important of all our digits is the thumb. Its ability to oppose the other fingers is a feature that distinguishes humans from most other animals and makes our hands so much more useful to us.

Long thumb flexor (flexor pollicis longus)

This muscle is found on the forearm, connecting the end of the thumb to the forearm and upper arm bones. It bends the thumb in towards the base of the index finger.

How to test

(*See Figure 23*) The athlete is seated with the arm straight and the thumb bent so that the end of the thumb is level with the base of the index finger. Hold the middle bone of the thumb and gently uncurl the end bone of the thumb.

HELP
Massage points

1 Behind the nipple on the chest wall.

2 Underneath the bottom angle of the shoulder-blade on the back.

Points to hold

Frontal eminences – either side of the forehead between the centre of the eyebrow and the hairline.

Sports problems

These muscles are especially used in speedway, cricket, racket sports and baseball.

Exercise

Weights – latissimus dorsi pulls, dumb-bells.

Short thumb flexors and adductors

Adductor pollicis

Description and test

This muscle holds the straight thumb against the palm under the index finger. Test by holding the athlete's hand from the back and pulling the straight thumb away from the palm. (*See Figure 24*)

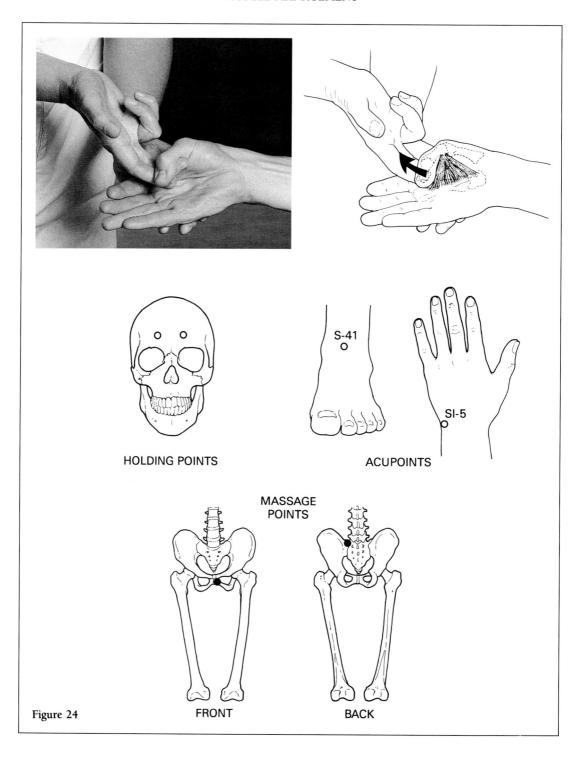

HOLDING POINTS

ACUPOINTS

S-41

SI-5

MASSAGE
POINTS

Figure 24

FRONT

BACK

Opponeus pollicis

Description and test

This muscle bends the base of the thumb in towards the little finger side of the palm. Test by holding the athlete's palm on the little finger side, the athlete pulls the base of the thumb across. Test by taking hold of the thumb joint nearest the wrist and pulling gently outwards. (*See Figure 25.*)

These two muscles help each other and yet they have different nerve supplies. When they are weak it is important to check for carpal tunnel and pisiform/hamate syndromes (see Chapter 6).

General test

Another way of testing these muscles is for the athlete to hold the thumb and little fingertips of the hand together, so as to make a ring. Test by hooking one finger from each hand round the athlete's thumb and little finger and gently pulling apart. Do not use the whole hand to hold the athlete's fingers as you will overpower them and cause damage.

There will be some 'give' because there are so many joints involved, but the muscles should still lock. This is a good general test, but be aware that you are also testing little finger muscles. The difficulty with this test is to determine which of the muscles is weak. Watch whether the thumb or little finger gives way first. (*See Figure 26.*)

The other fingers

Description

The main finger flexors are found on the forearm. One group flexes the second bone of each finger and the other flexes the last bone of each finger. These muscles will not usually be involved in carpal tunnel or pisiform/hamate syndromes (see Chapter 6).

How to test

(*See Figure 27*) The athlete's wrist must be in a neutral position, bent neither up nor down. Bend the finger at the first joint on the finger (not at the base of the finger). Test by holding the base of the finger with one hand and gently straighten the finger with your other hand. Alternatively, the athlete bends the last joint of the finger. Test by holding the first two bones of the finger with one hand and gently uncurl the last joint of the finger with your other hand.

HELP

Massage points

1 Under the pubic bone on the front of the pelvis.
2 Between the seventh and eighth ribs on the left side of the rib cage just inside the cartilage.
3 The most prominent knobs on the top of the back of the hips (L-5-PSIS).
4 Either side of the spine, level with the bottom of the shoulder-blade (seventh–eighth thoracic vertebrae).

Points to hold

1 The frontal eminences – either side of the forehead half-way between the middle of the eyebrow and hairline.
2 Half an inch (1.3 cm) above the posterior fontanel – the 'baby's soft spot' on the back of the head.
3 Acupoints SP-2 and H-8. SP-2 is on the nail side of the large joint at the base of the big toe, at the side of the foot. Hold it at the same time as H-8 which is on the palm of the hand on the crease below the ring finger.

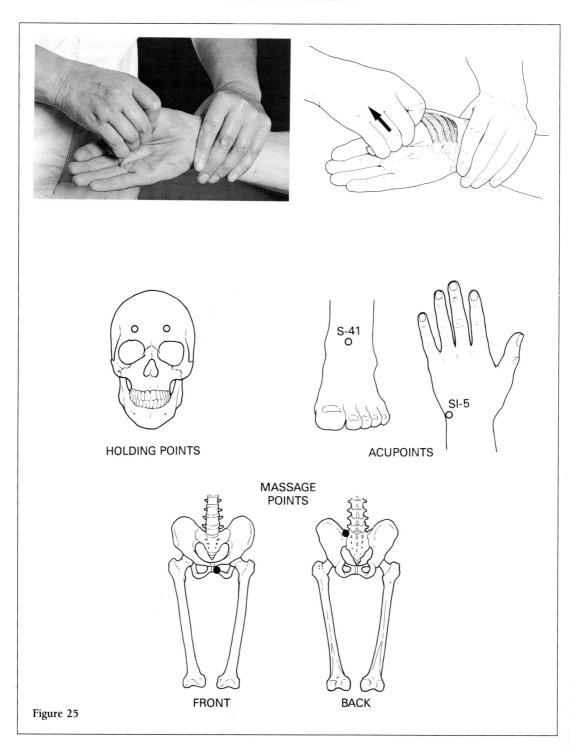

HOLDING POINTS

ACUPOINTS

S-41

SI-5

MASSAGE
POINTS

FRONT

BACK

Figure 25

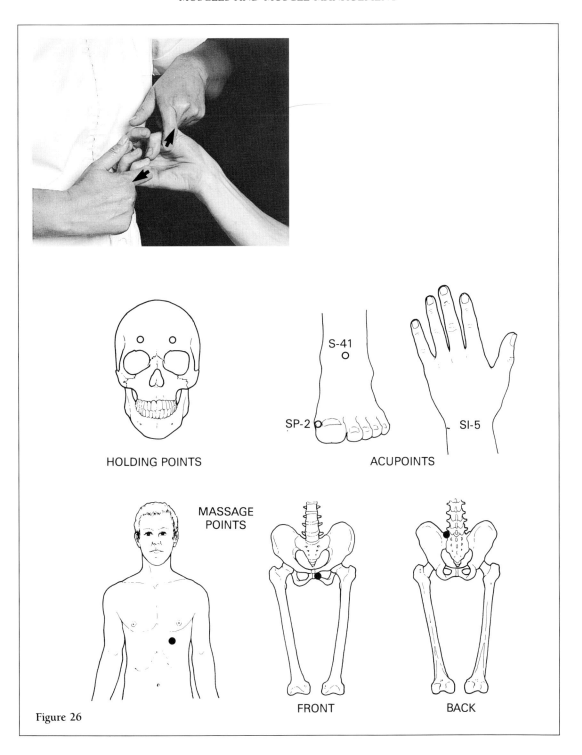

HOLDING POINTS

ACUPOINTS

S-41

SP-2

SI-5

MASSAGE POINTS

FRONT

BACK

Figure 26

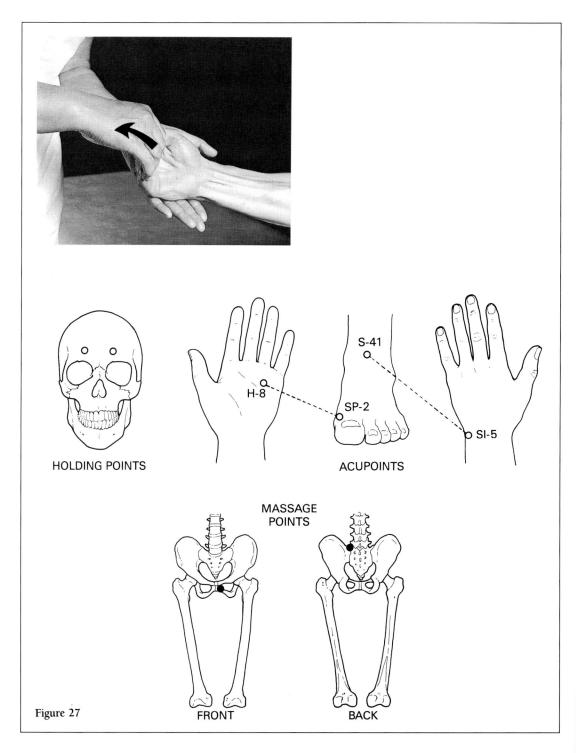

HOLDING POINTS

H-8

S-41

SP-2

SI-5

ACUPOINTS

MASSAGE
POINTS

Figure 27

FRONT

BACK

Hand flexors

These are used in lobs in racket sports, archery, rowing, in golf and rock-face climbing, high bar gymnastics, judo, baseball.

Exercise

Weights – press-ups, dips, shoulder and bench press, biceps curls, wrist rolls, chinning and latissimus dorsi pulls.

Hand extensors

These are used in backhand (badminton) and in golf and speedway.

Exercise

Weights – dumb-bells, wrist rolls.

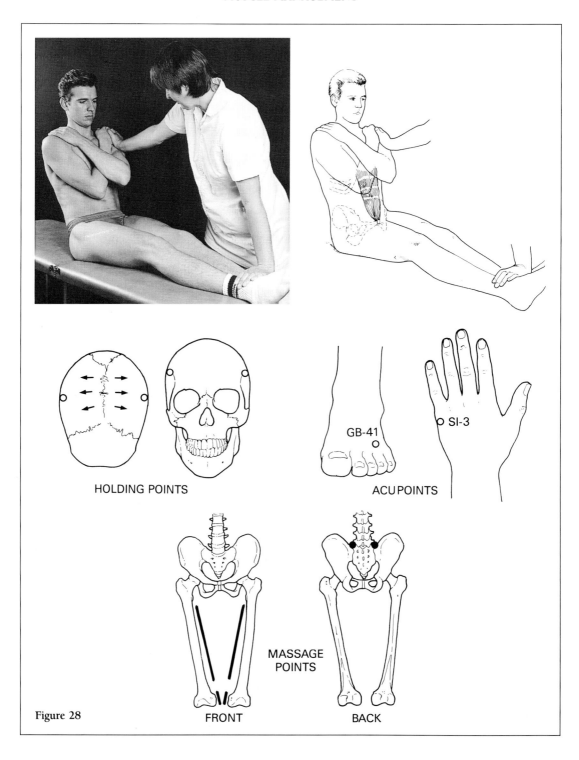

HOLDING POINTS

ACUPOINTS

GB-41

SI-3

MASSAGE POINTS

FRONT

BACK

Figure 28

FRONT ABDOMEN MUSCLES
Abdominals and pyramidalis

Description

The abdominal muscles including pyramidalis are very important for a number of reasons. Mainly they give stabilization to the spine in front by joining the pelvis and rib cage. Secondly, they support the digestive organs by compressing the abdomen. There are three main divisions: rectus abdominis, which has fibres running vertically from the front of the pubic bone to the bottom of the rib cartilage either side of the breastbone; the transverse and oblique abdominals run diagonally, joining the lower ribs on one side of the body to the pelvis the other side (they are involved when the upper spine is twisted against the hips); pyramidalis is found lower down and has a similar function to the transverse abdominals, but is more active when the upper part of the body leans forward.

How to test

Rectus abdominis
(*See Figure 28*) The athlete sits with legs straight and arms crossed so the hands are on the shoulders, lean back a little, but keeping the back straight and head up. Pressure is put against the wrists where they cross to push the torso backwards whilst you stabilize the legs. (This can also be done with the knees raised, in which case the knees need to be stabilized.)

Generally speaking, to test the various divisions of rectus abdominis, the further back you lean the higher up the abdomen the fibres being tested. To test one side at a time (the obliques), position as above, but push straight back on the shoulders one at a time.

Tranverse abdominals
(*See Figure 29*) These are tested by positioning as above (leaning back), but at the same time twisting the upper torso to one side and pushing the forward shoulder straight back (not along the line of the shoulder). Twist the other way to test the other side.

Pyramidalis
(*See Figure 30*) This is tested by positioning as for transverse abdominals, but leaning forward: push each shoulder back.

Other muscles to test if abdominals are weak: sacrospinalis, quadriceps, hamstrings, diaphragm, gluteus medius and maximus, psoas, latissimus dorsi.

HELP
Massage points

1 The inside of the thighs, a broad band stretching from knee to groin. The lower part will help rectus and pyramidalis most, the upper will help transverse and obliques most.
2 The most prominent knobs on the top of the back of the pelvis, level with the lowest lumbar and posterior superior iliac spine (PSIS).

Points to hold

1 The parietal eminence – 3″ (8 cm) above the ear at the widest point of the head.
2 Spread your fingers out either side of a line running centre front to back of the skull, pulling gently outward, as the athlete breathes in and pushes upward with his/her head. Do this five times. (This assists the normal motion of the bones of the skull in breathing.)
3 Acupoints GB-41 and SI-3. GB-41 is three fingers' width back towards the ankle from the joint of the fourth and little toe. Hold it together with SI-3, which is on the side back of the hand half-way between the base of the little finger and the wrist, where the first crease is found.

Diet

Foods rich in Vitamin E will help. Avoid spicy food, caffeine, alcohol, sugar, white flour and white rice.

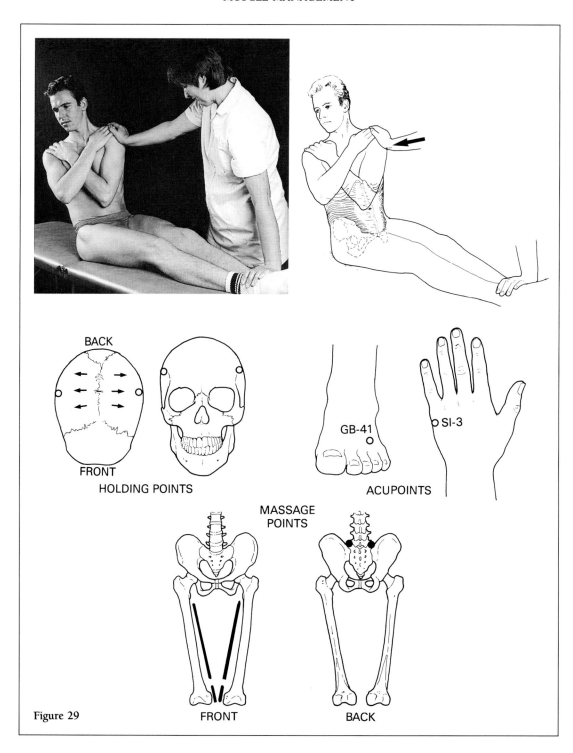

BACK

FRONT

HOLDING POINTS

GB-41

SI-3

ACUPOINTS

MASSAGE
POINTS

FRONT

BACK

Figure 29

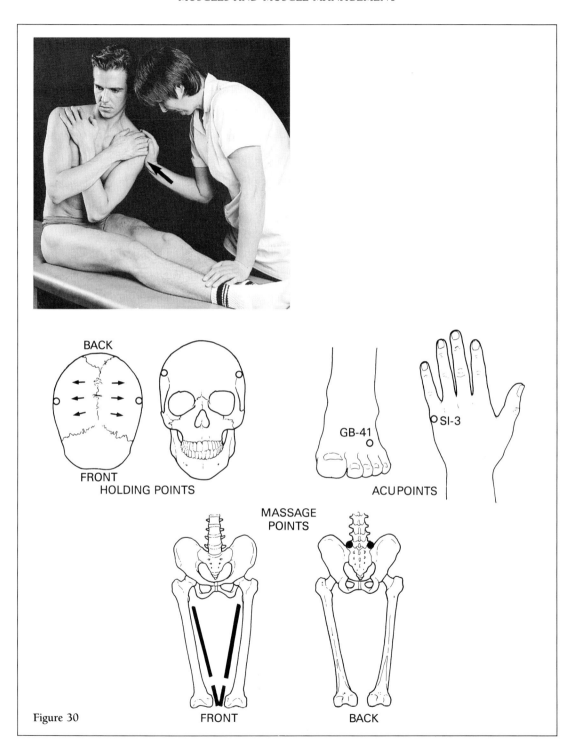

BACK

FRONT
HOLDING POINTS

GB-41

SI-3

ACUPOINTS

MASSAGE
POINTS

FRONT

BACK

Figure 30

Sports problems

These muscles are commonly involved in stomach aches, stomach cramps and, because of their nearness to the diaphragm, with breathing difficulties. Weakness can also result in low back pain, neck and shoulder problems and restricted shoulder movement. Weak abdominals need exercising, even though they respond to the rubbing and holding points. Doing sit-ups with the knees apart is a good conditioner. Abdominal muscles are used in so many sports, often one-sidedly, as in javelin, pole-vault, golf, hurdling and hockey. Obliques are used in canoeing, gymnastics and rugby.

Often they are used mistakenly when the quads are weak in skulling. Flabby 'beer-belly' is a sure sign of weakness. If the athlete has bloating and flatulence, check their diet and add garlic and charcoal to the list above.

The most common injury to the abdominals is when a part of the intestine bulges and pushes out through the muscle. This is known as a hernia, so it is vital to wear a belt when doing heavy weight-lifting. In very weak muscles even coughing will do this. If you suspect a hernia, get the athlete to see a doctor.

Exercise

Sit-ups, leg raises, standing alternate toe touch, side bends, lateral twists.

Pectoralis major (sternal division) (PMS)

Description

This is one of the chest muscles which runs from the groove between the muscles at the front of the upper arm across to the breastbone. It is responsible for drawing the arm in and down and turning the arm so that the palm faces outwards. These muscles are the part of the 'pecs' that body builders love to exhibit.

How to test

(*See Figure 31*)

Test position 1
The athlete lies on his or her back, extends the arm at right angles to the body, keeping the elbow locked straight, the palm facing outwards and the thumb pointing towards the feet. Stabilize the opposite hip. Pressure is put on the forearm to push the arm away from the opposite hip, i.e. push up and out to 45° (half-way between straight back and out to the side).

Test position 2
The athlete sits, extends his or her straight arm directly in front and parallel to the floor and with the palm turned away from the body, thumb pointing to the floor. Stabilize the opposite shoulder whilst you push up and out on the forearm at 45° (between horizontal and vertical). Watch that the body does not twist.

Other muscles to test if PMS is weak: PMC, anterior deltoid, infraspinatus, popliteus, anterior serratus, latissimus dorsi, subscapularis, teres major. Also check rhomboids for hypertension.

HELP
Massage points

1 Just under the nipple, between the fifth and sixth ribs on the right side of the chest.
2 Between the fifth and sixth ribs just to the side of the spine at the back (this is level with about half-way down the shoulder-blade).

Points to hold

1 In the hairline above the forehead just outside a line up from the middle of each eye.
2 Acupoints LV-8 and K-10. LV-8 is in the dip on the inside of the knee joint between the extreme end of the thigh bone and the hamstring tendon. Hold it together with K-10, which is almost next-door at the most inside end of the knee crease when the knee is bent.

Diet

Long-lasting headaches, photophobia (dislike of bright lights), spots in front of the eyes and general

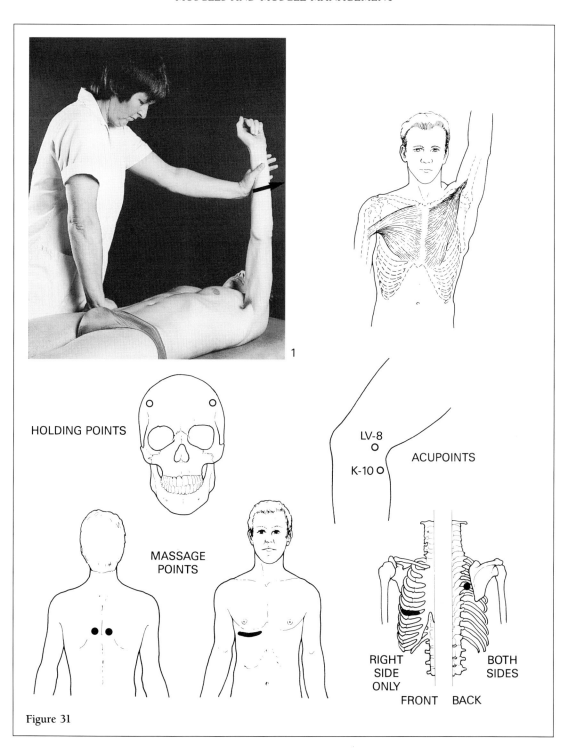

HOLDING POINTS

MASSAGE
POINTS

LV-8
K-10

ACUPOINTS

RIGHT
SIDE
ONLY

BOTH
SIDES

FRONT   BACK

Figure 31

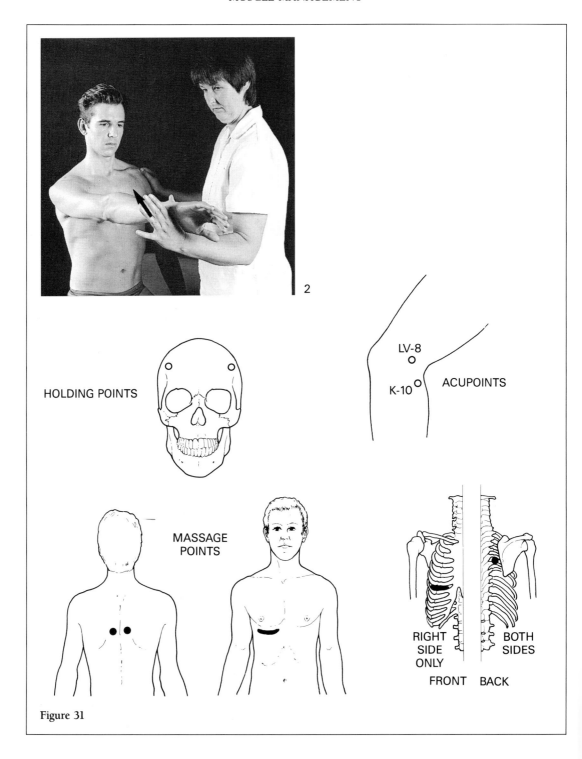

2

HOLDING POINTS

LV-8

K-10 ACUPOINTS

MASSAGE
POINTS

RIGHT
SIDE
ONLY

BOTH
SIDES

FRONT BACK

Figure 31

liverishness will all contribute to a weak PMS. Instruct the athlete to avoid fatty and fried foods, fizzy drinks and alcohol and all drinks containing caffeine. Eating liver and foods containing Vitamin A will help.

Sports problems

PMS is used in chin-ups and rock climbing, bowling, swimming, rings and high bar, judo and cricket, tennis – forehand and serving. All of these can be overdone, leading to fatigue and consequent tearing and shoulder problems. Be aware, too, that pain in this area can indicate heart or lung problems. (Don't be afraid to have this checked by a doctor – better safe than sorry!) It can also be due to referred pain from the liver.

Exercise

Push-ups, pull-ups, throwing, bench presses, chin-ups.

Weights – latissimus dorsi pulls and chest exercises.

Pectoralis major (clavicular division) (PMC)

Description

This muscle is the other half of PMS and is used in pulling the arm in and upward towards the opposite ear. It is attached on the front inside of the arm at the very top just below the shoulder and runs across the front of the armpit and chest wall to the collar-bone.

How to test

(*See Figure 32*) Start with the same position as for PMS – the athlete lies on his or her back, extends the straight arm at right angles to the body, in front. The palm is turned outward. This time, pressure is put on the wrist to push the arm outwards and downwards towards the feet at an angle of 45° (away from the opposite shoulder) whilst you stabilize the opposite shoulder to prevent the body twisting.

Other muscles to test if PMC is weak: PMS, middle trapezius, latissimus dorsi, pectoralis minor, sartorius.

HELP

Massage points

1 Under the left nipple between the fifth and sixth ribs on the chest wall.
2 Either side of the spine at the level of the fifth and sixth ribs.

Points to hold

1 Frontal eminences – above the centre of each eye, half-way between the eyebrows and the hairline.
2 Acupoints S-41 and SI-5. S-41 is on the top middle front of the ankle in a small dip. Hold it together with SI-5, which is just below the wrist on the edge of the hand (little finger side) on the end of the ulnar bone.

Diet

This muscle reacts very badly to upset tummies, allergies and food sensitivities; and above all to mental stress. It is important to reduce stress levels and not eat when upset. Particularly don't overload the stomach before a big match and don't let the athlete eat that last-minute sugar or sweet thing! It may give them instant energy but the long-lasting effect will be to drain them of B vitamins (needed to digest sugar products) and which also help to handle stress better. The net result, together with an overload of sugar in the blood, will cause too much insulin to be produced and the athlete will end up with a deficit of sugar in his or her blood an hour or so later just when they most need it for stamina. The answer is not to eat more sugar and continue the yo-yo of sugar levels, but to eat slow-release carbo-hydrates, like whole grains. (For more information, see *Diet for Runners*, by Nathan Pritikin.) Advise the

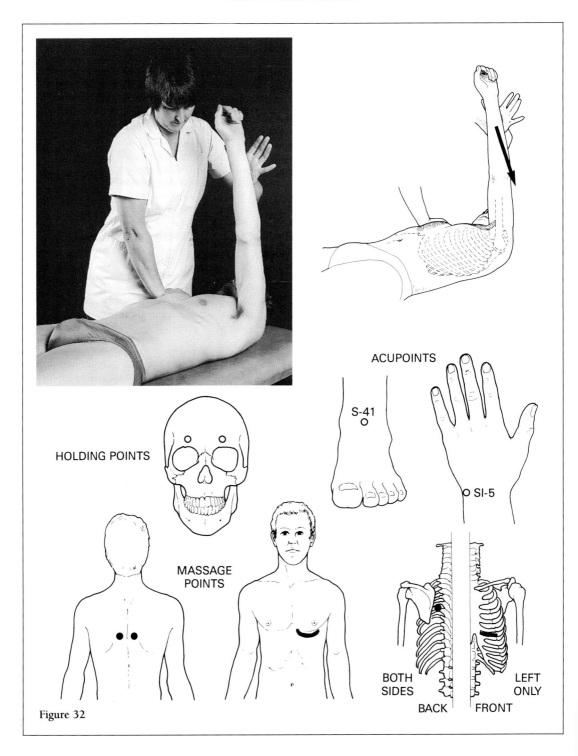

HOLDING POINTS

ACUPOINTS

S-41

SI-5

MASSAGE
POINTS

BOTH
SIDES

LEFT
ONLY

BACK   FRONT

Figure 32

athlete to eat foods containing Vitamin B in all its forms.

Sports problems

Stress is such a major problem in sport that it is discussed in detail in Chapter 7. If this muscle is continuously weak, turn to this chapter for further help. This muscle is used in so many sports –

bowling, curling, forehand in racket sports, cricket, golf, hockey, weight-lifting, etc. Weakness causes shoulder problems and chest pains.

Exercise

Push-ups, pull-ups, throwing, bench presses.
  Weights – latissimus dorsi pulls, chest exercises.

Diaphragm

Description

The diaphragm is one of the few horizontal muscles in the body dividing the torso of the body into two compartments – the top filled by the lungs and heart and the lower filled by the liver, spleen and all the digestive organs. It is attached to the inside of the lower ribs at the front and goes round the sides and to the back and has three large holes for the main blood vessels and the gullet to pass through and some smaller gaps for things like nerves. It is the main breathing muscle and alters the pressure around the lungs to make you breathe in and to help you to hold your breath in.

How to test

This muscle is difficult to test because it is rather inaccessible. There are various methods that involve blowing into things such as a spirometer etc. to test vital capacity. In the interests of simplicity, however, it works reasonably well to take a good breath in, hold it in and time it. The athlete should be able to hold it for at least 40 seconds. You can also push up with your fingers under the xiphoid process (where the ribs meet the bottom of the breastbone) whilst you test another strong muscle such as PMS. If PMS alone is strong but goes weak when you push up under the xiphoid, then the diaphragm may be weak too.

Other muscles to test if diaphragm is weak: abdominals, upper trapezius, pectoralis minor, neck muscles, teres minor, psoas.

HELP
Massage points

1 The whole length of the breastbone.
2 On the right side of the spine where the tenth rib joins it – this is on a level of about 2″ (5 cm) below the tips of the shoulder-blades. (*See Figure 33.*)

Points to hold

1 The bregma – the spot just back from the centre top of the head, where the frontal and two parietal (side) bones of the skull join. You can find it by putting the heel of your hand on the bridge of your nose – where your middle finger now falls on the top of your head is the place you want. Take care if you are doing this on a small person and you have large hands – you will go too far back! If in doubt, use the athlete's own hand.
2 Acupoints SP-3 and L-9. SP-3 is found on the big-toe side of the foot just heelwards of the meta-tarsal head – the main joint at the base of the big toe that so often becomes a bunion. Hold that point together with L-9, which is found on the wrist crease at the base of the thumb. These points may increase the time you can hold your breath by up to half as long again!

Diet

It goes without saying that if the athlete has lung problems they should not smoke. If they do smoke – perhaps to calm the nerves – turn to Chapter 7

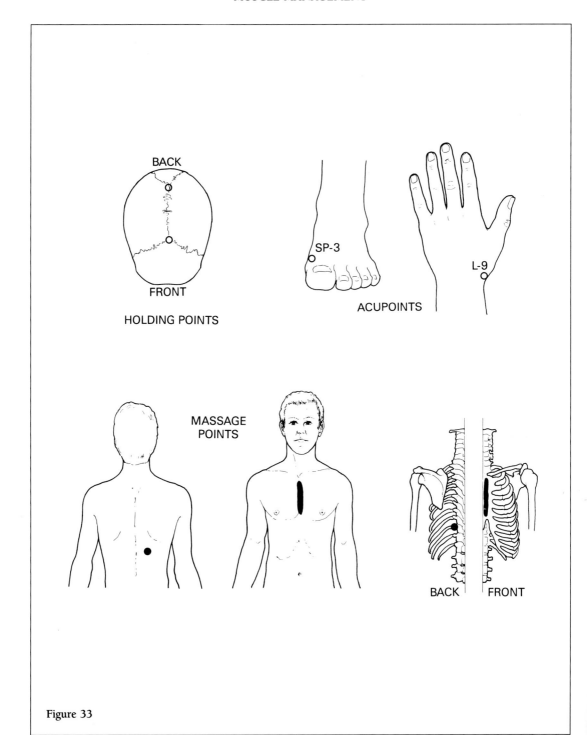

BACK

FRONT

HOLDING POINTS

SP-3

L-9

ACUPOINTS

MASSAGE
POINTS

BACK | FRONT

Figure 33

where advice is given on stress relief and stress management, and which may help them to break the psychological dependency (which is much harder to control than the nicotine dependency).

If the athlete has a weak diaphragm they may also have digestive disturbances. Sometimes part of the stomach can get pushed up through the diaphragm and cause 'heart burn'. If this is the case, advise the athlete to eat smaller meals (little and often) rather than fewer large meals and not to sit curled up afterwards to watch TV!

Foods rich in Vitamin C will help.

Sports problems

A weak diaphragm can cause abdominal weakness and lead to digestive problems. But, beyond these, it goes without saying that lung capacity and breath control is vital in all sports. It is extraordinary how many people almost stop breathing when they are trying hard and yet that is the one time the brain and muscles need oxygen! If, on the other hand, the athlete feels tight-chested and panicky, they should talk to their trainer and doctor about it. Read the relevant section in Chapter 7 on stress and pre-plan to help to reduce their panic. The use of acupoints to increase breath hold are of vital importance to swimmers and divers.

Exercise

Abdominal breathing exercises.

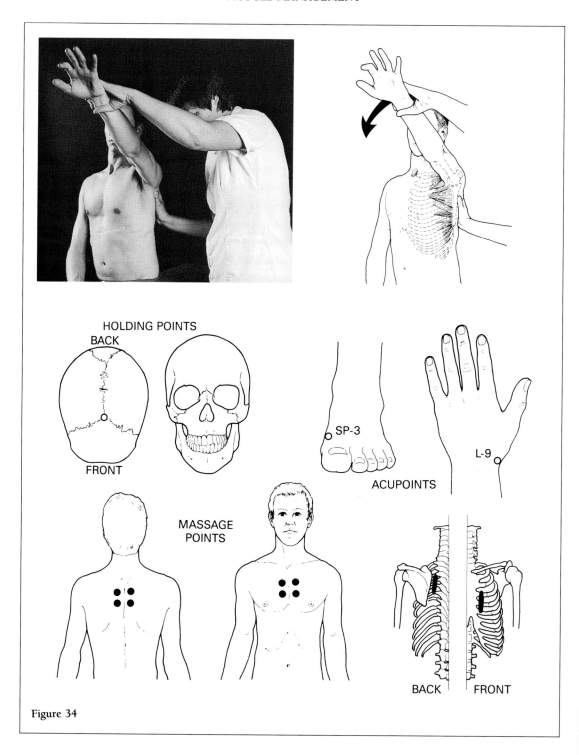

HOLDING POINTS
BACK
FRONT

MASSAGE
POINTS

SP-3
L-9
ACUPOINTS

BACK   FRONT

Figure 34

BACK OF THE BODY MUSCLES

Anterior serratus

Description

This muscle is the serrated one you see like a zig-zag line on the ribs at the side of the body. It has fibres attached to the top eight or nine ribs at the side of the body. The fibres run under the shoulder-blade and attach to its inner border, so when the muscle contracts the whole shoulder-blade is pulled and tipped so the shoulder joint is fixed at the point where the upper arm fits into the joint socket (glenoid cavity). It also holds the shoulder-blade onto the rib cage helped by rhomboids and middle trapezius.

How to test

(*See Figure 34*)

Test position 1
Sit or stand with the arm held out straight in front and 45° to the side, the thumb pointing up. Hold the shoulder-blade tip up and don't let it slide as the arm is pushed down.

Test position 2
The athlete lies on his or her back and raises the arm straight up at 90° with the thumb pointing towards the head. Slide one hand under the shoulder-blade and pull it outwards to prevent it moving as the arm is pushed down towards the feet with your other hand.

Other muscles to test if anterior serratus is weak: deltoids, coracobrachialis, diaphragm, rhomboids, levator scapulae.

HELP
Massage points

1 Between the third, fourth and fifth ribs close to the breastbone on the front and
2 Either side of the third, fourth and fifth vertebrae level with the top and down to the middle of the shoulder-blades.

Points to hold

1 The bregma – the spot just back from the centre top of the head, where the frontal and two parietal (side) bones of the skull join.
2 Acupoints SP-3 and L-9. SP-3 is the instep side of the big joint at the base of the big toe. Hold it at the same time as L-9, which is at the base of the thumb.

Diet

The athlete should be encouraged to drink more water and eat foods rich in Vitamin C. Plenty of fresh air is good. Advise the athlete to keep away from smokers and dirty or mouldy atmospheres and check for allergies to the substances they normally eat or have around at home. They should avoid all dairy products. All of the above is relevant because the anterior serratus appears to be an indicator of lung function if it is constantly weak.

Sports problems

No one will deny the need for good lungs and oxygen distribution in the body for all sports. When anterior serratus is weak there is often poor lung function and shoulder-blades wing out when the athlete leans with their arms straigth out against a wall. A weak anterior serratus will also lead to shoulder problems and the athlete will find it hard to hold his/her arm out in front for any length of time or carry any weights at arm's length. This will make martial arts particularly difficult, also hockey and ice-hockey, let alone doing press-ups and parallel-bar work, boxing or shot-putting.

Exercise

Push-ups, pulling weights from behind at arm's legnth. Swimming on your back.
    Weights – bench press, shoulder press.

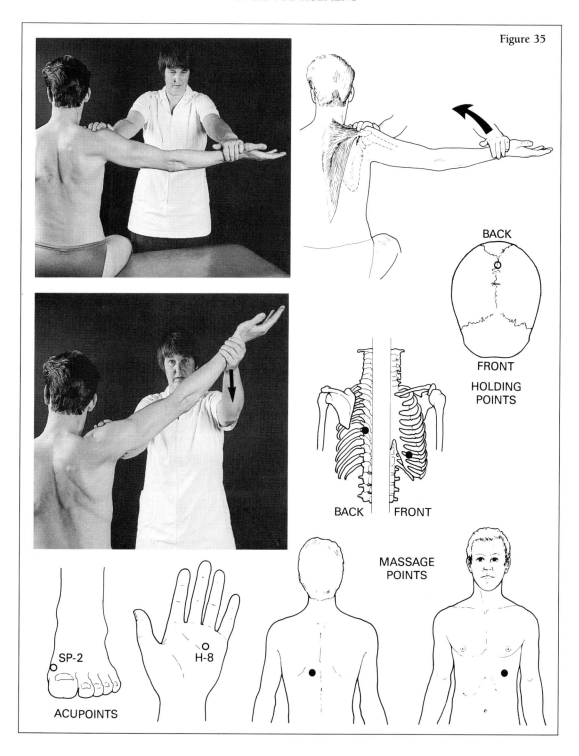

Figure 35

BACK

FRONT

HOLDING POINTS

BACK   FRONT

MASSAGE POINTS

SP-2

H-8

ACUPOINTS

Middle and lower trapezius

Description

There are the two lower divisions of the kite-shaped muscle that stretches from the middle of the back to the back of the head and out to each shoulder. The upper division has its own discussion (see pages 28–30). Middle trapezius runs from the top five vertebrae of the back to the ridge in the middle of the shoulder-blade. It keeps the shoulder-blade in and turns it.

Lower trapezius runs from the sixth to the twelfth thoracic vertebrae (directly under the middle trapezius) to the ridge in the middle of the shoulder-blade. It rotates and stabilizes the shoulder-blade, drawing it in and helps keep the mid-spine upright.

How to test

(*See Figure 35*) The athlete lies face down near the edge of the table, the arm extended 90° out to the side. For middle trapezius the arm should be turned so that the thumb points to the head and the elbow faces the feet. Pressure is put on the upper arm to push the arm to the floor, whilst the opposite shoulder is stabilized. For the lower trapezius the arm should be turned even more (as far as possible) and raised 45° towards the head. Pressure is put on the upper arm to push it to the floor whilst the opposite hip is stabilized. In both cases you are simply using the arm as a lever via the shoulder-blade to test the muscle.

Other muscles to test if trapezius is weak: anterior serratus, rhomboids, PMC, upper trapezius and levator scapulae.

HELP
Massage points

1 Between the seventh and eighth ribs on the left – just below the level of the end of the breastbone.
2 On the back on the left side of the spine between the seventh and eighth thoracic vertebrae, level with the bottom of the shoulder-blades.

Points to hold

1 1½" (3 cm) behind the bregma, well back from the centre top of the head (1" above the lambda).
2 Acupoints SP-2 and H-8. SP-2 is found on the nail side of the big-toe joint on the side of the foot. Hold it at the same time as H-8, which is on the palm of the hand on the crease below the base of the ring finger and little finger.

Diet

These muscles have an association with the spleen and with sore throats and anaemia. Buckwheat and foods high in Vitamin C and calcium will help.

Sports problems

These muscles are often involved in shoulder and arm problems, but also mid-back problems. Pain and weakness can also refer from neck disturbances (as a result of over-short pectoralis minor), or the spine in the upper back being pushed out of alignment through over-use on one side (as in one-sided sports such as racket sports, golf, cricket, etc.).

Weakness causes difficulty in lifting or bending the upper arm and pain in pectoralis major clavicular. It can also lead to sore throats, hearing loss and blood disorders.

Exercise

Moving weights overhead with extended arms, shoulder shrugs with weights in the hands, rowing.

ERRATA

Page 84/85 The text describes the lying test, whilst the illustrations show the sitting test. In the sitting test the arm is pulled directly towards the tester.

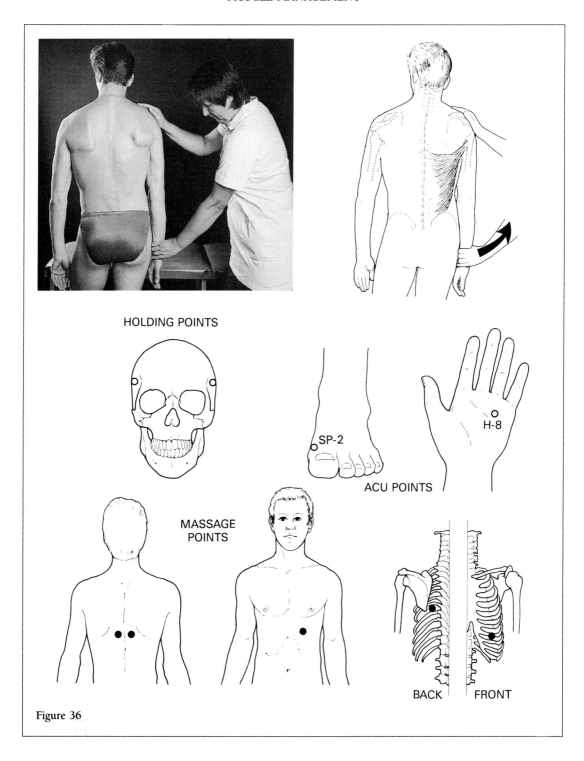

HOLDING POINTS

SP-2

H-8

ACU POINTS

MASSAGE
POINTS

BACK   FRONT

Figure 36

Latissimus dorsi

Description

This is one of the big muscles of the back. It is joined to the pelvis and lower and middle spine by a very strong sheet of cartilagenous tissue. It narrows down to a single, very strong tendon that catches the bottom tip of the shoulder blade as it passes and twists round on itself, going under the armpit and attaching to the front of the upper arm. This means it twists the arm inwards and holds it to the body. It also helps to hold the shoulder blade down and in against the body (slightly) and gives the power to pull the torso up in chin-ups, keeping the back straight.

How to test

(*See Figure 36*)   The athlete can stand or lie. Twist the athlete's arm so that the palm faces outwards. Be sure the elbow is locked straight and that the torso has not changed position or the shoulder raised. Pull the forearm away from the body as you stabilize the shoulder. Some people can over-straighten the arm, others are unable to do so completely – this is not the object of the test, so make sure the arm is as straight as it will go (even ask the athlete to hold in with the elbow, *not* the wrist, as you test).

Other muscles to test if latissimus dorsi is weak: upper trapezius, pectoralis major clavicular, triceps, sartorius, gracilis.

HELP

Massage points

1 Between the seventh and eighth ribs on the left side of the front near the edge of the rib cage – usually about 1½–2″ (4–5 cm) below the nipple and 1″ (2.5 cm) in towards the middle of the body.
2 Between the seventh and eighth ribs either side of the spine on the back. This is usually about level with the bottom of the shoulder-blade.

Points to hold

1 On the parietal bone about 1″ (2.5 cm) above the top of the ear and slightly back.
2 Acupoints SP-2 and H-8. SP-2 is on the outside edge of the big toe, just toe-nail side of the big joint. Hold it at the same time as H-8, which is on the palm of the hand on the crease under the ring and little finger.

Diet

A constantly weak latissimus dorsi may be an indicator of difficulty with sugar digestion such as diabetes, hyper-insulinism or low blood sugar. In these days when sugar appears in so many foods and in the most unexpected places it is not surprising that this muscle weakness is extremely common. The athlete must avoid all extra sugar like the plague and be aware that it is a normal constituent of cooked, processed and packaged meats, ham, sausages, salamis, sauces, tinned vegetables and fruit, all cakes, pastries and biscuits, bottled and packaged juices and juice concentrates. The best forms of sugar are those that release slowly into the bloodstream, such as fruit sugars (fructose) found in raw fruit and honey and molasses.

Teach the athlete to look out for and avoid names such as maltose, sucrose, glucose, syrup, dextrose and all the other 'oses' as they all deplete the body of vitamin B and they will end up feeling tired and depressed. If athletes feel they lack stamina and need extra energy, feel tired, irritable and dizzy, they should eat whole grains (as advised by Pritikin – see Bibliography). It is a good idea to avoid stimulants such as caffeine and alcohol as they raise the blood-sugar level too fast, too. Eating foods such as tripe and sweetbreads and all foods containing Vitamins A and F will help. Lowering adrenaline output will also help, so athletes must cut down on stress and worry.

Sports problems

This muscle is used in golf, tennis, swimming, rings, climbing, rowing and may be involved in frozen shoulder. By far the most common problem, though, is over-use – practising a specific technique of your sport over and over again on muscles already weak from too much sugar intake. Weakness on one side only, for instance, will cause an inability to swim and turn straight at speed. Continually having to correct direction saps strength and can mean second place instead of first. Pain in the elbow is common with a weak latissimus dorsi, as the athlete will try to hold the arm in with arm muscles instead.

Exercise

Chinning, dips on parallel bars and rings, rope-climbing.

Weights – seated rowing and latissimus dorsi pulls.

Sacrospinalis or erector spinae

Description

This is really a composite muscle made up of many parts, like the rigging of a mast on a ship. It joins the ribs to the spine, ribs to other ribs, the pelvis to the ribs and ultimately the pelvis to the spine, the back of the head and neck. It can also be said to include all the tiny muscles that join one vertebrae to the next or to the one or two beyond that. It is often blamed for, and strengthened, because of back pain when it is not at fault at all! (See below.) It balances the abdominal muscles to keep the spine upright against gravity. It extends the spine when bending back-wards and helps to rotate it; and when contracting one side and not the other it either bends the spine or the pelvis sideways.

How to test

(*See Figure 37*) The athlete lies face down. The hands are placed across each other and resting back down on the back of the pelvis. The athlete then lifts both shoulders off the table and looks to one side. Test by stabilizing the opposite hip and push the shoulder the athlete is looking over, to the table. Swop stabilization, head turn and shoulder push to test the other side.

Other muscles to test if sacrospinalis is weak: latissimus dorsi, quadratus lumborum, psoas, abdominals (especially transverse), gluteus maximus, hamstrings, quadriceps, anterior tibials, peroneus.

HELP

Massage points

1 Either side of the belly button and over the middle of the pubic bone on the front of the pelvis. (Rub the bone, don't squash the bladder!)
2 The edges of the second lumbar vertebrae level with just below the lowest part of the rib cage, but next to the spine, or count up three vertebrae from the most prominent knobs on the pelvis which are level with the fifth lumbar.

Points to hold

1 The frontal eminences – the prominent bumps on the forehead between the centre of each eyebrow and the hairline.
2 Acupoints B-67 and L-11. B-67 is found on the nail of the little toe on the outside. Hold at the same time as L-11, which is on the thumb side of the nail of the index finger.

Diet

Because it is a big composite muscle it can be helped by several sorts of nutrition, especially Vitamins A, C, E and calcium.

Sports problems

I am not talking here about wear and tear, disc damage, stress fractures or spondylolysthesis, etc. for which you need a doctor, chiropractor, osteopath or

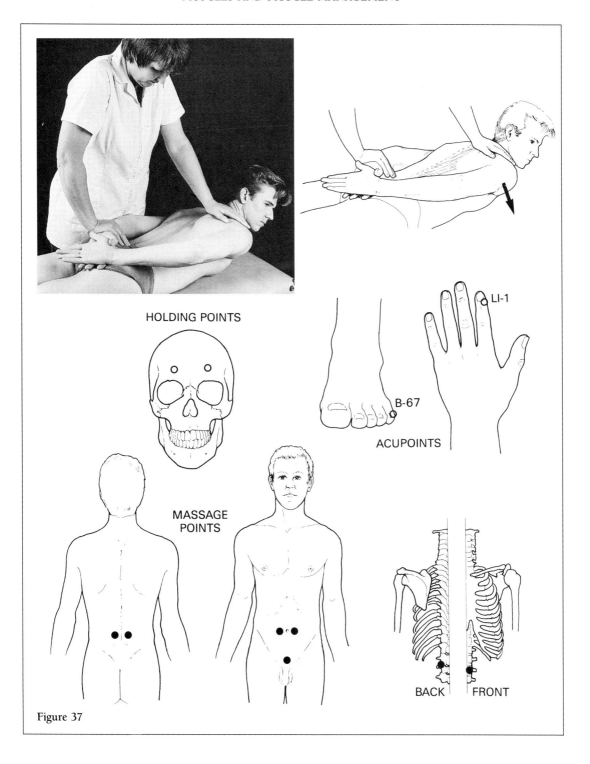

HOLDING POINTS

LI-1

B-67

ACUPOINTS

MASSAGE
POINTS

BACK   FRONT

Figure 37

surgeon. A great deal of so-called 'arthritic' pain will improve if the athlete cuts out allergic foods and balances the muscles by the 'help' points here. So often sacrospinalis is blamed for back pain when the problem is really weak abdominals and the poor back muscles are having to do all the work of supporting you against gravity alone. No wonder they complain, spasm and go on strike (lumbago!). Strengthen abdominals and release the sacrospinalis from its misery!

True weak sacrospinalis can cause nineteen different areas of pain and malfunction such as arthritis, rheumatism, sciatica and referred pain, numbness and tingling in the legs and feet, bursitis, shoulder and elbow problems, restricted movement and, if weak one-sided and long standing, will cause a 'C' curve or scoliosis (S-bend sideways) in the spine.

Scoliosis is most common in youngsters as they reach maturity and should be watched for, as it can set in for life. The other main cause of sacrospinalis malfunction is one-sided sports such as racket sports and cricket, but worst are probably golf and rowing which combine pull and twist.

It is noticeable that athletes who feel they are not being supported by their coaches, trainers, teammates, family and friends do tend to develop backache as though their body is acting out the distress they feel. Psychological it may be, but very real and very painful, nonetheless. If you feel this might be a contributing factor, turn to Chapter 7.

A less common cause of sacrospinalis malfunction is bladder problems and infections. To help this, always wear cotton underwear, drink plenty of camomile tea and barley water; eat melon and pumpkin seeds, lots of garlic and avoid sugar, caffeine, chocolate, rhubarb and purple fruits, spicy food and anything to which the athlete is allergic. If you have to take antibiotics, watch out for rashes, nausea, depression, diarrhoea and headaches; and when you finish the antibiotics eat lots of live yoghurt.

Backs are used in all sports, whether it be in bending to pick up a golf tee or weight-lifting. In all cases, if you have problems, you are unbalanced muscularly, misusing your back, or your technique is at fault. It may be that you are unaware of where your hip joint is – no, it is *not* at the waist but a good hand-span below it at the front/sides. Your legs are not an extension of your body, the body is slung between them in the pelvis. Therefore when you bend, let your body go between your legs, use your leg muscles – especially the big thigh muscles – to support you and the weight you are lifting. Use them to straighten you up and *not* the smaller multiple sacrospinalis fibres that happen to cross the low back area. Whenever possible, use your feet to turn your body rather than twist your spine. Good foot work and flexible knees are the secret of a good back. Watch any child of 1½–2 years old. They know how to bend efficiently. It is us adults who have adulterated our movement!

A final cause of back problems is the bed we sleep in and the chair we have to sit in (whether the car seat or the easy chair we slouch in to watch TV after training). The best seats are at right angles with a level or slightly forward-sloping seat and good support for the lumbar spine. Chairs are made for average people, with poor average posture – which of us is average and who wants poor posture? Car seats are rarely custom-made and in some smaller popular models the brake and clutch are 'offset' to save space so that you have to twist to drive. Athletes can't expect to arrive in good shape to win their 'away match' after that!

The only thing the trainer can advise is to get a wedge-shaped cushion or fold up a hand towel and sit on it or against it, so that the seat fits the athlete, and they are not forced to fit the seat! At first it may not feel so comfortable to sit well if their muscles are not used to it, but two hours later they will notice how alert they are compared with the others (who thought they were relaxing and are now fidgeting and wriggling in their seats and feeling tired and uncomfortable because their backs are not properly supported);

The only criteria for judging whether athletes have the right mattress on their bed is for them to lie on their side and ask someone to look and see if their spine is straight. If it isn't, the mattress is too hard or too soft. It should take up the curves and not vice versa! A short-term help to get over this is to ask for an extra pillow and put it under your waist when you lie on your side to fill up the gap instead of letting your spine sag to one side.

Exercise

Lateral bending. Get the athlete to lie on his/her stomach and lift the feet and shoulders off the table

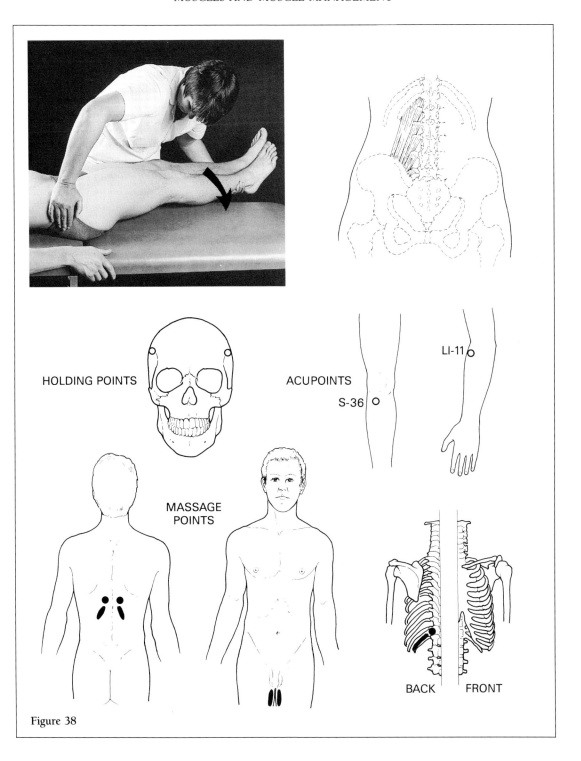

HOLDING POINTS

ACUPOINTS

S-36

LI-11

MASSAGE POINTS

BACK   FRONT

Figure 38

- if you can, do it with arms and legs straight (back extension exercise).

Weights – latissimus dorsi pulls, squats, back squats.

Quadratus lumborum

Description

This muscle is found in the lower back and joins the back of the pelvis to the lower spine and the lowest rib. It helps sacrospinalis and also stabilizes the lower back. When contracted on one side it can pull the upper body down to the hip on that side. It also helps the diaphragm in breathing by stabilizing the bottom rib.

How to test

(*See Figure 38*) The athlete lies on his or her back and whilst stabilizing the upper body by gripping the table, swings the leg out to the side from the hips. Stabilize the opposite hip whilst you push the legs (on the ankles) in again. How far out you take the legs will depend on which fibres you want to test. The further out the legs are taken, the lower the fibres down towards the pelvis are tested. A general test taking the legs out 10° will do, however. Watch that the athlete doesn't try to rotate the pelvis to try to bring other synergist muscles into better alignment, especially gluteus medius.

Other muscles to test if quadratus lumborum is weak: the obliques of the abdominals, sacrospinalis and psoas, iliacus, popliteus.

HELP

Massage points

1 The top 6″ (15 cm) inside the upper thigh.
2 The most prominent knobs on the back of the pelvis, level with the fifth lumbar vertebrae (PSIS).
3 The end of the twelfth ribs.
4. Between the last two lowest ribs next to the spine.

Points to hold

1 Parietal eminence – a spot 3″ (7.5 cm) above the ear at the widest point on the head.
2 Acupoints LI-11 and S-36. LI-11 is found at the end of the elbow crease on the thumb side. Hold it at the same time as S-36, which is just outside the bump below the knee cap (on the front of the shin) and about 2″ (5 cm) to the outside of the knee.

Diet

Foods rich in vitamins A, E and C may be helpful.

Sports problems

In severe weakness lateral bending will be very difficult. A good way to compare each side is to see, while keeping the back and pelvis as square to the front as possible, just how far the athlete can reach when sliding their hand down the side of one leg compared with the other. As with sacrospinalis, this muscle too is often blamed for low back problems that are more properly abdominal weakness. It can, however, cause back pain, chest and abdominal pain and stomach upset.

Stiffness in this area can wreck a good seat and is directly transmitted to the horse in riding. It is also used in gymnastics, especially in working on the pommel horse, swinging the hips and legs relative to the position of the upper body.

Exercise

Lateral bending

PELVIC MUSCLES

Psoas

Description

This muscle connects the inside of the lower spine to the thigh bone, running across the edge of the pelvis in front as it does so. Therefore it's a hip flexor because it draws the thigh bone forward and is the first muscle used in bringing the leg forward in a running stride. It also helps stabilize the sacroiliac joint.

How to test

(*See Figure 39*)   The athlete lies on his or her back with one straight leg raised 45° and taken out to the side 45°. The foot is turned out. Press against the inside of the leg to push out and down whilst stabilizing the other hip so that the body doesn't rock. Watch, too, that it is not showing weak because you are putting pressure on an old knee injury.

Other muscles to test if psoas is weak: iliacus, upper trapezius, tensor fascia lata, gluteus medius, sacrospinalis.

HELP
Massage points

1 Measure 1″ (2.5 cm) out and 1″ (2.5 cm) up from tummy button on the front of the body (both sides).
2 On the back either side of the spine about 2″ (5 cm) higher (T-12/L-1).

Points to hold

1 Find the top of the little valley at the back of the neck where it joins the head. Go diagonally up and out about 1″ (2.5 cm) either side of the prominent bump at the base of the skull.
2 Hold acupoints K-7 and L-8. Hold three fingers up from inner ankle and ½″ (1.2 cm) back towards heel, together with three fingers away from inner wrist crease on thumb side.

Diet

This muscle is badly affected by coffee and dehydration so avoid all forms of caffeine – including chocolate and cola – and drink plenty of water (particularly if the athlete works in a centrally heated environment where there's coffee on tap). Eat food containing vitamins A and E.

Sports problems

Psoas is very important in lumbago, nagging low back pain, sway-back (or lordosis) and curved spine and may be involved in disc problems. Where it crosses the hip girdle at the front there is a bursa (or friction pad) which can be irritated and inflamed by too much long-distance running, sprint training, hill running, speed skating, hurdling and squat thrusts.

A weak muscle shows up often with an outward flicking of the foot in the swing phase of the gait. Weakness both sides can lead to flat back and flat feet or other foot problems. Walking and running with ankles turned in can cause strain to the low back. If both psoases are weak, suspect a bang to the back of the head, which will switch both muscles off. Look out for this in sports such as rugby, lacrosse, hockey, high jump, etc. Psoas is particularly used in hurdling, sprinting, diving and long jump.

Exercise

Encourage athletes to do leg raises whilst lying on their back, running and jogging, lifting the heels high.

Psoas bounce – place one foot and knee well forward and one leg back straight, keeping the torso upright, bound up and down and then stay down a while to stretch psoas.

Weights – hip flexions, sit-ups, squats, quads, knee extensions.

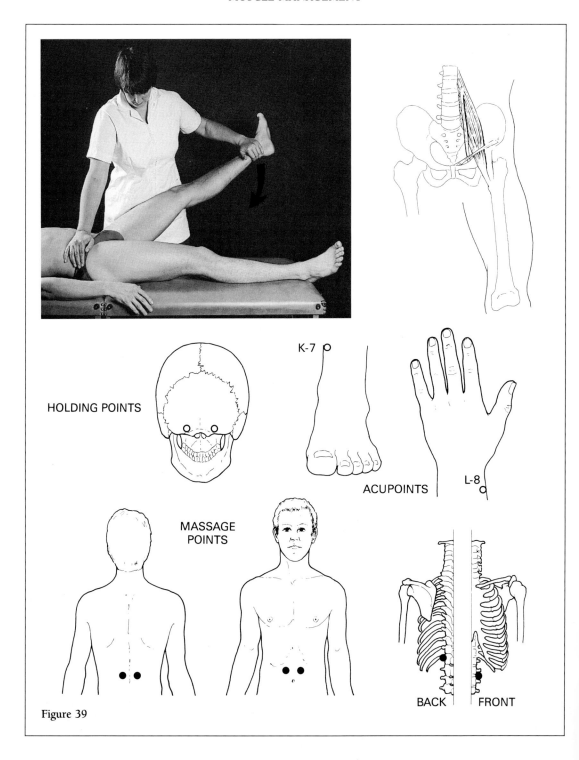

HOLDING POINTS

K-7

ACUPOINTS

L-8

MASSAGE POINTS

BACK   FRONT

Figure 39

Iliacus

Description

This muscle is often combined with psoas as ilio-psoas because they have a common tendon and attach together on the inside of the top of the thigh bone. The other end of the muscle spreads round the inside of the bowl of the pelvis, inside the big bone felt when you put your hands on your hips. This means it pulls the thigh bone up both from the sides and the back.

How to test

(*See Figure 40*)   Because it pulls from two directions, there are several ways to test this muscle. Where the weakness is found will depend upon which of the muscle fibres is upset or damaged.

Test position 1
Lie the athlete on his or her back. Twist the foot out to the side and lift it straight up to the ceiling. Stabilize the other side of the body (on the hip perhaps) with one hand whilst you push the leg back straight down, making sure there is no bend at the knee and watching for knee injury or rocking of the hips to recruit other muscles. (Tell the athlete to 'hold up'.) This test tests the muscle fibres nearest the spine.

Test position 2
As above, but lift the leg as high as possible. Stabilize the other hip and push the raised leg out to the side. This tests the fibres furthest from the spine.

Test position 3
Lie the athlete on his or her stomach. Bend the leg at the knee to 90° and let the foot drop out to the side as far as it can (this will vary enormously depending upon the athlete's flexibility). Pressure is put on at the ankle to bring it back towards the middle, whilst stabilizing the knee. (Tell the athlete to 'hold the foot out'.)

N.B. Notice the difference in angle between psoas test and Test position 2 above, which lifts the leg higher and pushes *out* more than *down*.

Other muscles to test if iliacus is weak: psoas, tensor fascia lata, adductors, quadratus lumborum. Check gluteus maximus and quadratus lumborum are not hypertense.

HELP
Massage points

1 Inside the front edge and round to the side of the hip bone.
2 The dip on front of the shoulder where the arm joins the body.
3 On the mid back next to the spine at the level of the last rib (L-1/T-12).
4 1″ out and 1″ up from the tummy - as for psoas.

Points to hold

1 The parietal eminence, which is the widest part of the head, one hand's width directly above the ear.
2 Acupoints: same as psoas (*see Figure 39*). Hold K-7 and L-8 together.

Diet

If this muscle is weak it is often the result of dietary indiscretion or stress which results in digestive upsets and may indicate iliocaecal valve malfunction – a very common problem for athletes, as it can be triggered by mental and physical stress as well as diet.

Sports problems

Marathons of any sort can cause malfunction of the iliocaecal valve. By this I don't just mean 26-mile runs, but extra long matches, hard five sets at tennis or extra time after a score draw at football on heavy turf, or other similar situations. Often the mental stress prior to a big match will cause the problem mildly, which will then cause the iliacus muscles to be weak before the start. Then the extra physical stress of effort to win 'the big match' can lead to injuries during and problems afterwards (especially if they lose). Watch for this problem if the athlete has

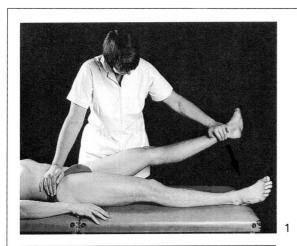

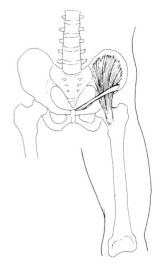

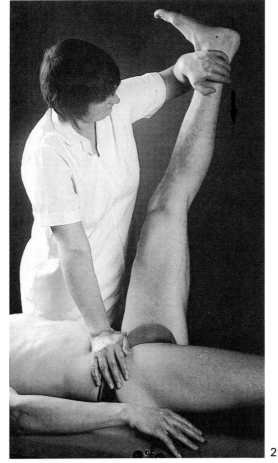

Figure 40

Page 97   The arrow in the photograph should indicate that the direction of pressure on the ankle is to bring it (back) towards the middle of the other leg.

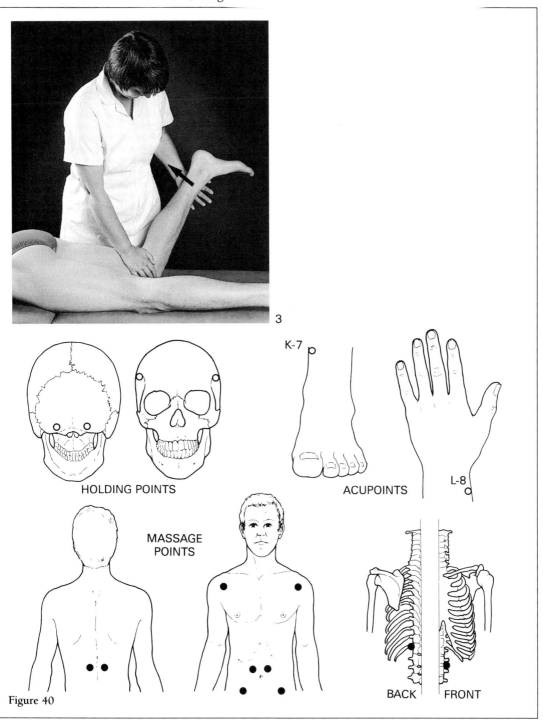

3

HOLDING POINTS

K-7

ACUPOINTS

L-8

MASSAGE POINTS

BACK   FRONT

Figure 40

diarrhoea often. Turn to the notes of ileocaecal valve in Chapter 6. However, if they get sharp and increasing pains in the right groin area, it is vital that they see a doctor to eliminate appendix problems. The site is almost the same and if the appendix goes wrong, it can be life threatening.

Exercise

Leg raising whilst lying on the back, running and jogging, lifting the legs high.

Piriformis

Description

This is one of the buttock muscles, but although it's a postural muscle its fibres run horizontally across the sacro-iliac joint (which is where the spine fits on to the hips). One end is attached to the sacrum and the other is attached to the top outside of the thigh bone. You contract piriformis when you sit and spread your knees out sideways. If you stand and clench your buttocks you are using the other buttock (gluteal) muscles too.

How to test

(*See Figure 41*)

Test position 1
The athlete lies on his or her back with knee and hip bent at right angles. The ankle is then taken in across the other leg. Pressure is applied on the inside of the ankle to push the ankle out to the side whilst stabilizing the knee.

Test position 2
The athlete lies face down and bends the knee at right angles whilst rotating the thigh, so that the ankle comes across the other leg. Pressure is then put on the inside of the ankle to push it out sideways whilst you stabilize the outside of the knee.

Test position 3
The athlete sits, knees bent at a right angle and the lower leg taken across so that the ankle is over the other ankle (not one knee over the other). Pressure is then put on the inside of the ankle to push it outwards and return it to a straight position.

Other muscles to test if piriformis is weak: gluteus maximus, tensor fascia lata, hamstrings, adductors.

HELP

Massage points

1 Top of the pubic bone.
2 The most prominent knobs on the back top of the hips (posterior superior iliac spine (PSIS) and L-5).

Points to hold

1 Parietal eminence – a point 3″ (7.5 cm) above the ear at the widest point of the head.
2 Acupoints LV-1 and CX-9. LV-1 is on the big toe-nail bed on the side nearest the other toes. Hold it together with CX-9 which is the end of the middle finger pad on the side nearest the index finger.

Diet

Foods rich in vitamins A and E will help.

Sports problems

Weakness on one side can cause the sacrum to twist, the ankle on that side to turn in, the knees knock and the opposite foot to turn out. It is also worth checking piriformis if there is any suggestion of sciatic pain, twisting or burning, tingling or numbness in the leg anywhere or burning urination. This is because piriformis runs very close to, surrounds, is above or below the sciatic nerve and can squeeze or stretch it, causing referred pain. Piriformis (and gamelli and obdurators) are used in breaststroke and football.

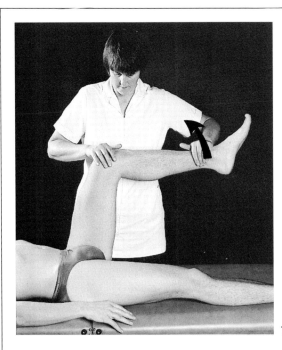

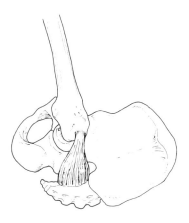

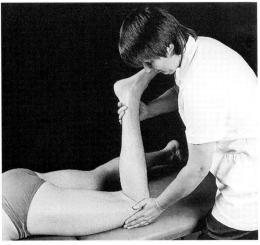

Figure 41

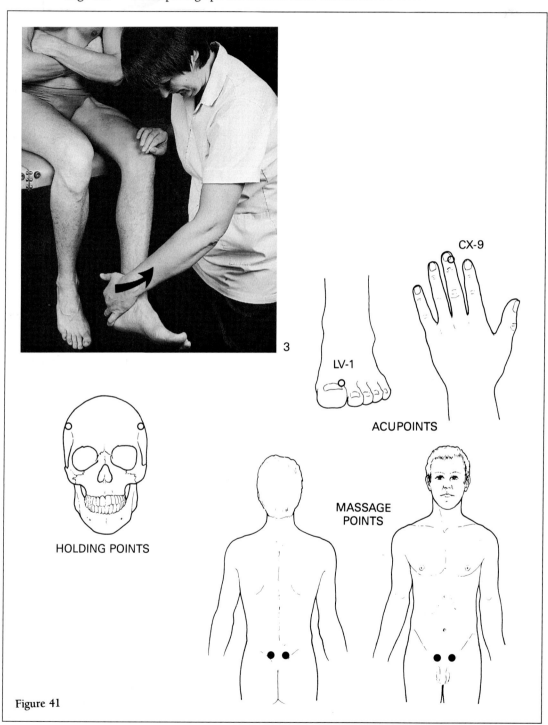

3

CX-9

LV-1

ACUPOINTS

HOLDING POINTS

MASSAGE
POINTS

Figure 41

Exercise

Stand on one leg and, keeping the foot firmly on the ground, twist the body above the knee from side to side.

Check piriformis, too, if the athlete can't put one ankle on top of the other knee when sitting as the muscle may be hypertense on that side.

Many people who have to have their arms relaxed for their particular sport hold and display tension in buttocks instead of the shoulders. A good test for this is to press in the dimples on either cheek of the buttocks. Sharp pain here means tension and pressure on the sciatic nerve.

One-sided running sports such as hurdling (or in sports where the athlete takes off from one leg from an inward twist such as baseball and high jump or golf) are particularly prone to piriformis problems. Check which side is tightest and strengthen the opposite side.

Weights – low leg pulley.

Gluteus maximus

Description

This is the main seat or buttock muscle. It stabilizes the back of the hips as you step up a step. It prevents the pelvis tipping forward and, in this way, it helps the abdominals hold you upright against gravity on standing. It also helps the hamstrings and does the same job when the hamstrings are put out of action by bending the knees. It comes into action primarily when arching the whole body backwards and in running, hopping, skipping and jumping. It is attached to the sacrum and runs diagonally downwards to the top of the back of the thigh bone and also joins a common tendon with the tensor fascia lata.

How to test

(*See Figure 42*)   The athlete lies face down, the knee is bent at right angles so the foot is up in the air. Raise the whole leg off the table at least 6″ (15 cm). Pressure is put on the back of the thigh to push the leg back down whilst stabilizing the opposite hip or shoulder. Watch for change in the amount of knee flexion (the athlete is trying to use the hamstrings to help) or rolling the hip (to use quadratus lumborum).

Other muscles to test if gluteus maximus is weak: hamstrings, adductors and piriformis, gluteus medius, neck flexors and extensors.

HELP

Massage points

1 The whole length of the front of the thigh, slightly outside of centre.
2 Posterior superior iliac spine (PSIS) – the most prominent knobs on the back of the hip bones.

Points to hold

1 Lambdoidal sutre – a point 2″ (5 cm) behind the ear on an imaginary line extending from the corner of the eye through the top of the ear.
2 Acupoints LV-1 and CX-9 – LV-1 is on the nail bed of the big toe on the side nearest the other toes. Hold it together with CX-9, which is on the nail bed of the middle finger (nearest index finger side).

Diet

Eat foods rich in Vitamin E.

Sports problems

Weakness on one side will make the buttocks go off to one side, so be vigilant in sports that encourage this such as golf, constantly getting on and off horses (which is only ever done on one side).

Weakness on one side often means an extra tight

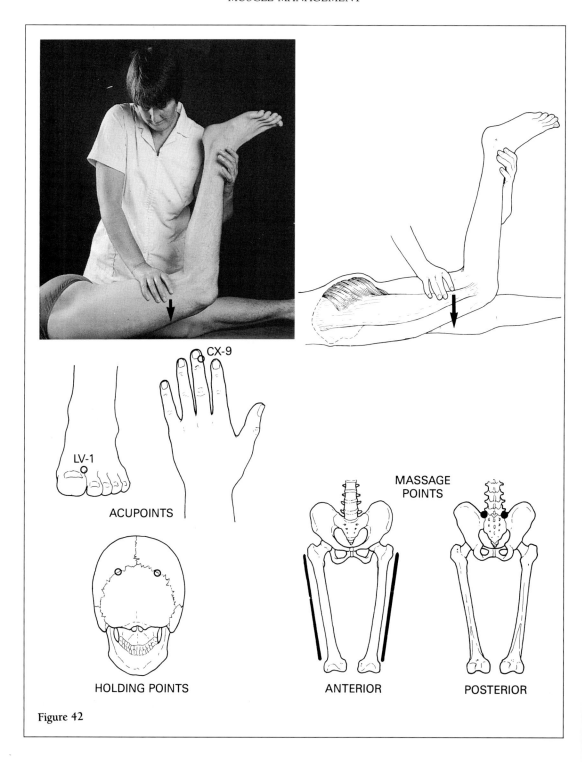

CX-9

LV-1

ACUPOINTS

MASSAGE
POINTS

HOLDING POINTS

ANTERIOR

POSTERIOR

Figure 42

muscle the other side and can lead to sciatic pain. Weakness both sides means walking will be difficult. There will be low back pain and it may also lead to a stiff neck and menstrual difficulties.

Although it is used in running, it should not be used in normal walking, except when going up and down stairs. Then, it only comes into use if there is an extra large abdomen as perhaps in wrestling or pregnancy. If it is used in this way it tends to make one look more sway-backed than ever as the buttocks protrude backwards. It is properly used in swimming, skating and ballet.

Exercise

The best way to develop and maintain this muscle is by running, skipping, hopping, jumping and squats.

Weights – hamstring curl.

Gluteus medius and minimus

Description

These two muscles work very similarly, so I'll consider them as one here. The muscles are found at the sides of the hips and consequently help prevent excessive swaying of the hips from side to side as you walk and run. They run from the outside of the hip bone down across the hip joint to the top outside of the thigh bone. They come into action in the weight-bearing leg when lifting the other to take a step. They are also hip abductors taking the legs out to the side.

How to test

(*See Figure 43*)

Test position 1
Test with the athlete lying on his or her back with the leg out to the side. Stabilize the other leg and, whilst making sure the athlete's heel doesn't hook over the table or drag on the table covering, keep the legs as near to the table as possible. If they are lifted too much you will almost be testing tensor fascia lata. Make sure the hips don't twist either to try and use tensor fascia lata as you push in towards the other leg.

Sometimes this muscle will only test weak in a standing position.

Test position 2
Have the athlete lean his or her hip against a heavy table to stabilize it while standing on that leg. Take the other out to the side and then push in towards the table. Watch out for hip twisting to try to use tensor fascia lata instead!

Test position 3
As (1) or (2) above, but with the foot turned out to the side as you push the leg in, back of the heel first. *Other muscles to test* if gluteus medius and/or minimus is weak: psoas, tensor fascia lata, piriformis.

HELP
Massage points

1 Upper edge of the front of the pubic bone.
2 The most prominent knobs on the back of the hip bone at the level of L-5 (fifth lumbar vertebrae).

Points to hold

1 Parietal eminence – 3″ (7.5 cm) above the ear at the widest part of the head.
2 Acupoints LV-1 together with CX-9. LV-1 is on the big toes near the corner of the nail bed on the side nearest the other toes. CX-9 is at the end of the middle finger pad on the side nearest the index finger.

Diet

If this muscle is constantly weak it may be an indication of poor glandular function, so support it by advising the athlete to eat foods containing Vitamin E.

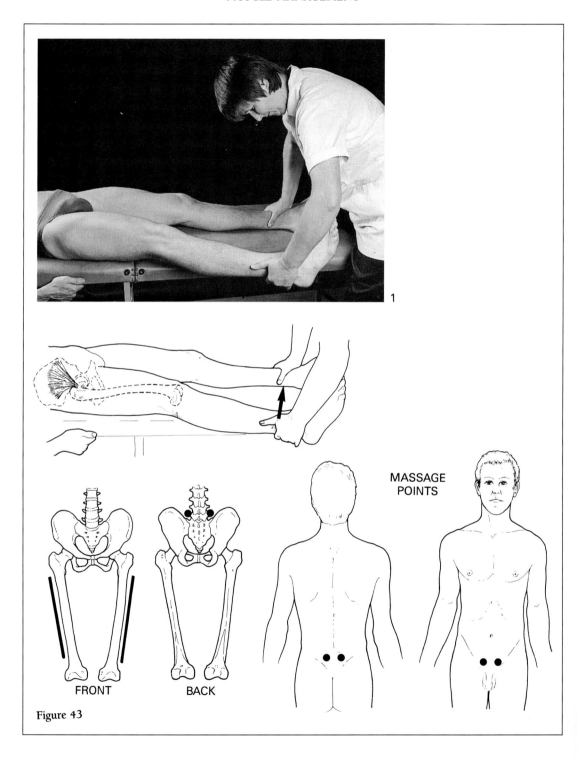

FRONT BACK

MASSAGE POINTS

Figure 43

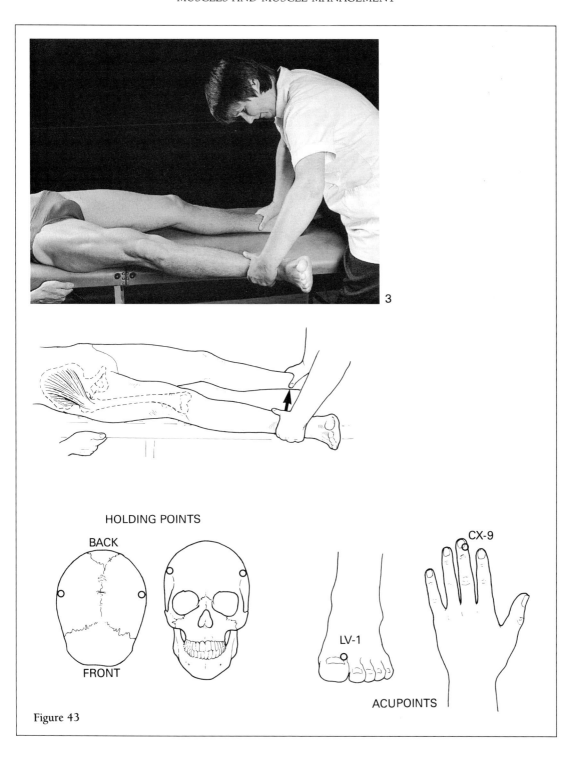

3

HOLDING POINTS

BACK

FRONT

CX-9

LV-1

ACUPOINTS

Figure 43

Sports problems

This muscle stabilizes the side of the hip and so is important in any sport where you have to stand on one leg, whether it be ballet, football, skating or running. If weak on one side it can lead to unbalanced hip and shoulder levels upsetting balance and eventually to limping, menstrual problems and breast soreness.

It is used most in skating and cross-country skiing.

Exercise

To strengthen it after working on the help points the athlete can:

1 Cross the ankles and pull one leg against the other.
2 Turn on their side and do straight leg rises keeping the foot pointed either forward or upward (*not* down and in, which will strengthen tensor fascia lata).
3 Run, hop on one foot and skip.

Weights – abductors and floor abductors as above.

FRONT AND INNER THIGH MUSCLES

Quadriceps

Description

The quadriceps is a group of four muscles found on the front of the thigh. Rectus femoris, vastus inter-medialis, lateralis and medialis. They extend the leg by straightening the knee and rectus femoris is also a hip flexor because it is attached to the hip bone in the front. The other three are attached to the thigh bone itself and all four muscles are attached at the other end by a common tendon below the knee, with the kneecap (patella) lying in the middle of that tendon and acting as a fulcrum to give extra strength.

How to test

(*See Figure 44*)

Test position 1
A general test is to sit on a table with one leg dangling over the side. The tester puts a hand under the knee to protect the hamstrings from the sharp edge of the table and as the athlete straightens the knee the tester pushes against the shin to bend the knee.

Test position 2
The athlete lies on his or her back and raises the thigh not quite at right angles to the body, the heel just above the horizontal. Allowing no inward or outward rotation of the thigh, push straight towards the feet to straighten the knee and hip.

Test position 3
(a) As (2) above, but angling the ankle inward so that the heel is over the other knee. Pushing along the line of the shin tests vastus lateralis.
(b) As (2) above, but angling the heel outside the line of the body and pushing along that line tests vastus medialis.
(c) As (2) above, but pushing down on the shin whilst stabilizing the knee to test vastus inter-medialis.
(d) As (2) above but with the leg straight and pushing the shin (keeping the leg straight!) down to the table tests rectus femoris. Remember that in each position the other muscles are working, too, but at a slight disadvantage.

Other muscles to test if quadriceps are weak: sartorius, tensor fascia lata, psoas, iliacus, abdominals, popliteus, sacrospinalis.

HELP

Massage points

1 All along the underneath of the rib cage in front.
2 Either side of the spine, from just below the level of shoulder blade (where the eighth rib is attached) to three ribs below. (T-8 to T-11)

Points to hold

1 Parietal eminence – the widest point of the head about 3″ (7.5 cm) above the top of the ear.
2 Acupoint SI-3 on the back of the hand, half-way between the ring and little fingers, knuckles and wrist. Hold this together with an acupoint GB-41, which is similarly placed on the top of the foot, half-way between the base of the fourth and little toes and ankle.

Diet

This muscle together with the abdominals, reacts badly to too much stress, especially when the brain has to compute too much new information or too many new sport techniques. Indigestion, bloating and gas that occurs on standing up can occur concurrently with this muscle weakness. It responds well to all the B vitamins. Avoid spicy food, refined carbohydrates, caffeine and alcohol. You may also find milk products difficult to digest if this muscle is often weak.

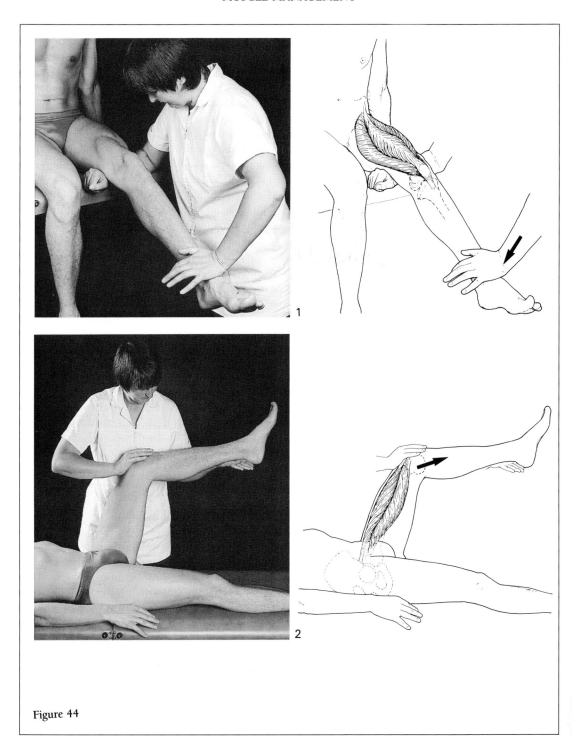

Figure 44

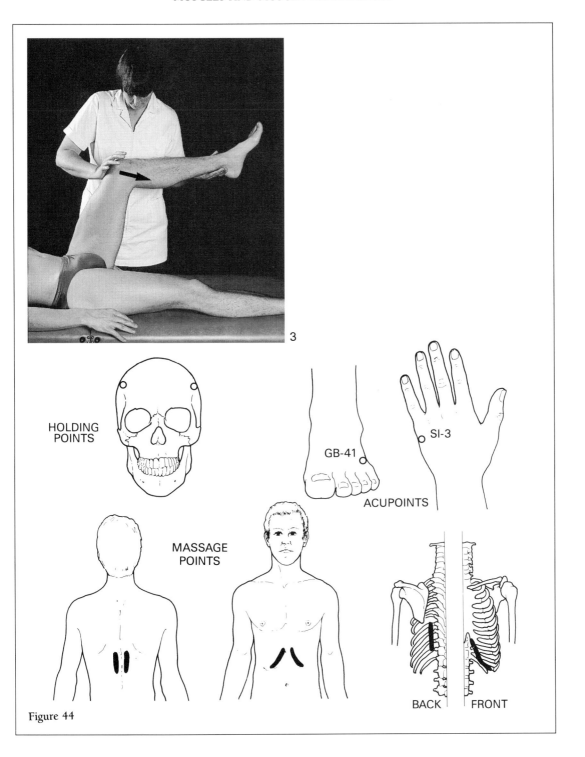

HOLDING
POINTS

GB-41

SI-3

ACUPOINTS

MASSAGE
POINTS

BACK   FRONT

Figure 44

Sports problems

Quadriceps work especially hard in sports that include running up hill, rowing, riding (especially rising in the saddle), cycling, shot-putt, weight-lifting, high jump, hurdling and gymnastics, football and skiing.

Exercise

Running, jumping, hopping, skipping, walking.

Weights – quadriceps knee extension exercise, leg press, back squats and squats.

Adductors and pectineus

Description

Adductors pull the legs inwards and mostly roll the thigh outwards slightly. The four main parts are pectineus and adductors brevis, longus and magnus. They all start at the pubic bone (or ramus) and attach at different heights along the inside of the thigh bone.

Pectineus   *ON TW Maredean*

How to test

(*See Figure 45a*)   The athlete lies on his or her back. The leg is raised with the knee bent until the heel rests by the knee of the straight leg. The bent knee is then held across the other thigh whilst pressure is applied to the inside of the bent knee to push it back out to the side again. The straight leg will need to be held to stabilize it and prevent hip rock.

HELP

Massage points

1 The middle of the pubic bone on the top.
2 The most prominent knobs on the back of the pelvis (L-5).

Adductors

How to test

(*See Figure 45b*)   The athlete lies on his or her back with legs straight and feet together. Pressure is applied on the inside to push the legs apart. Watch for hip rock to try to use other muscles, such as gracilis.

HELP

Massage points

1 Behind the areola between the fourth and fifth rib.
2 Just below the lowest point of the shoulder-blade, between the eighth and ninth ribs.

Points to hold for both adductors and pectineus

1 The parietal eminence, which is 3″ (7.5 cm) above the ear at the widest point of the head.
2 The lambdoidal suture – a point 2″ (5 cm) behind the ear which you will find if you draw an imaginary line from the eye through the top of the ear.
3 Acupoints LV-1 and CX-9. Hold the point LV-1, on the nail bed of the big toe nearest the other toes, together with point CX-9 on the middle finger-nail bed.

Other muscles to test if pectineus or adductors are weak: gracilis. Check opposing muscles, tensor fascia lata and hamstrings.

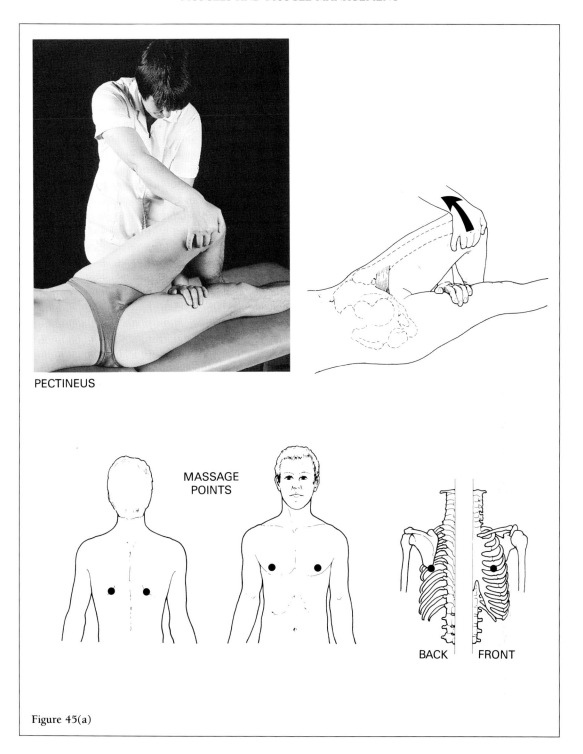

PECTINEUS

MASSAGE POINTS

BACK   FRONT

Figure 45(a)

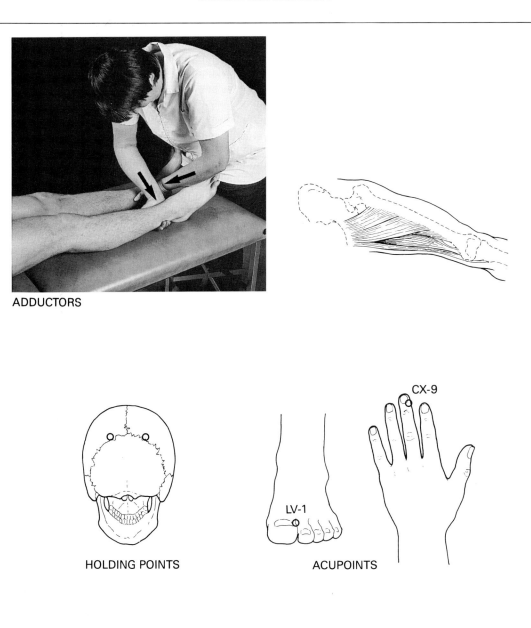

ADDUCTORS

CX-9

LV-1

HOLDING POINTS

ACUPOINTS

Figure 45(b)

Diet

Foods rich in vitamin E should be emphasized in the diet.

Sports problems

These muscles are used in all forms of horse-riding to grip with the knees. They are also used in kicking across the body in football, hurdling, swimming, judo and wrestling. Forcing the legs apart by slipping during skating or skiing or trying to do the splits or excessive turn out in pliés in dancing will cause injury to one or more areas of the adductors.

Don't forget that this area is particularly well supplied with lymph nodes that become clogged sitting all day at the office and so it's necessary to warm up well to get things flowing again. If you look at Figure 1 you will see that this lymph area affects a lot of other important postural muscles.

Weak adductors can also cause uneven hips which become low on the weak side, elbow pain and stiff shoulders and hormone problems. Pain in the area of the adductors can be referred from a back injury or pelvic misalignment, so if using the information in this book hasn't helped, the athlete should see a doctor or chiropractor to check their pelvis and spine, particularly if their sport is one-sided, like golf or tennis. So often it is the adductors which provide the 'strong leg' to hit against and take the strain of the hit.

Exercise

Riding, jumping jacks, swimming and jogging.
Weights – abductor machine, low leg pulley.

Sartorius

Description

Because it runs diagonally across the front of the thigh, sartorius helps to stabilize both the outside of the hip joint and inside of the knee, like cross-hatching, but since it crosses both hip and knee joints it helps quadriceps both as a hip flexor and knee extensor, too. You use sartorius most when you sit cross-legged, 'tailor fashion', or the stork position in yoga.

How to test

(*See Figure 46*) The athlete lies face up with leg turned out and knee bent so that the ankle lies over the other knee, or just below it. The tester holds the bent knee to stabilize it and push inwards slightly and then pulls against the ankle to straighten the leg. Take care the athlete doesn't hook his toes over the shin or round the knee.

Other muscles to test if sartorius is weak: adductors, gracilis, quadriceps, hamstrings, neck flexors, soleus, latissimus dorsi, gastrocnemius, pectoralis major clavicular, psoas, peroneus, sacrospinalis, anterior tibials.

HELP

Massage points

1 On the belly 1″ (2.5 cm) to the side and 2″ (5 cm) up towards the head.
2 Just above the lowest rib at the back, right against the spine (T-11-12).

Points to hold

1 The lambda – the spot on the back of the head where the occipital and the two parietal bones of the skull meet.
2 Acupoints T-3 and GB-41. T-3 is between the knuckles of the ring and little fingers and the wrist, one third of the way down from the base of the ring finger. Hold this together with GB-41, which is in a similar place on the top of the foot, between the base of the fourth and little toes and ankle.

Diet

Particularly if the athlete feels very tired in the

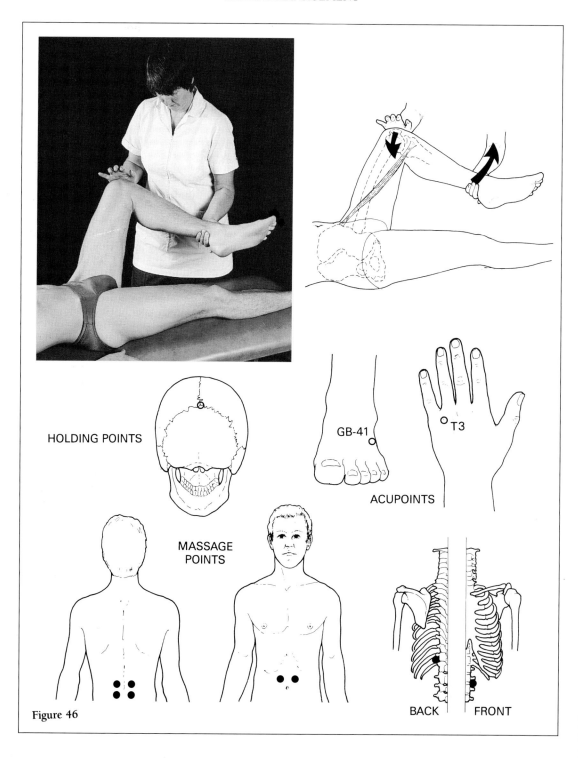

HOLDING POINTS

GB-41

T3

ACUPOINTS

MASSAGE
POINTS

BACK   FRONT

Figure 46

mornings but improves as the day goes on, or the blood pressure doesn't vary when standing up after lying down and this muscle is weak, the athlete must get help with his/her adrenals and check their sugar intake. (*Body Mechanics*, by Michael Lebowitz, contains an adrenal recovery diet. See Bibliography.)

When weak, this muscle can also cause the pelvis to twist so you don't face the front squarely. It can also cause knee pain. The athlete should eat foods with a high Vitamin C content and reduce their intake of chocolate, coffee and cola, all of which stress the adrenals. They must get plenty of sleep. When the body loses its ability to cope with stress because the adrenals are drained the immune system is weakened and the athlete becomes prone to all sorts of minor infections which will reduce athletic capabilities.

Taking cortisone over a period of time in the form of injections for inflammatory conditions or creams for itching and rashes can even lead to adrenal atrophy and depress the formation of white blood cells which protect you from infections and heal wounds.

The athlete may also have low blood sugar (hypoglaecemia), especially if the muscle is tender to touch.

This does not mean they should go and eat sugar lumps! Read Pritikin's *Diet for Runners* (see Bibliography) and switch them to a high-complex carbohydrate diet which releases carbohydrates (sugars) into the system slowly and consistently in a form that the body can handle and which will give stamina. Eating lots of sugar in lump form or in tea and coffee is disastrous, as too much gets into the blood supply too fast and the body over-reacts by pumping in insulin and the athlete ends up with even lower blood sugar!

Sports problems

Sartorius is an important muscle in hill running and kicking with the inside of your foot, as in football and some martial arts. It is also used in basketball and skating. Weak sartorius can cause knee pain, hip twisting, morning tiredness and swelling hands and feet due to water imbalance.

Exercise

Sit-ups with legs extended, walking, jogging.
   Weights – low leg pulley, abductor machine.

Gracilis

Description

Gracilis is an adductor because it draws the thigh inward. It is also a flexor as it draws the knee and hip together, too. It works together with sartorius. It is attached to the front of the pelvis underneath and runs down the inside of the thigh to just below the inside of the knee. It also stabilizes the inside of the knee joint.

How to test

(*See Figure 47*)

Test position 1
The athlete lies on his or her back. Turn the leg and foot inward as far as you can to stop the adductors working, and then pull the knee (or straightened leg) outwards.

Test position 2
The athlete lies face down, with the knee bent at 30°. Pressure is put against the inside of the calf near the ankle to push the foot out to the side whilst stabilizing the outside of the knee.

Other muscles to test if gracilis is weak: sartorius, quadriceps, adductors, hamstrings, latissimus dorsi, pectoralis major clavicular, psoas, neck flexors and sacrospinalis.

HELP

See *Sartorius* (page 113).

Diet

See *Sartorius*. Also check gracilis if swelling of the hands and feet is present, as there may be a water imbalance.

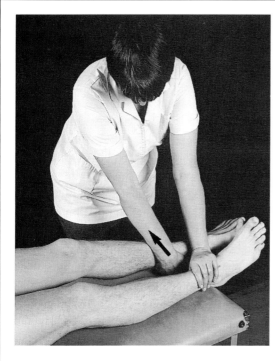

1

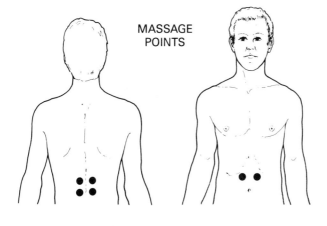

MASSAGE
POINTS

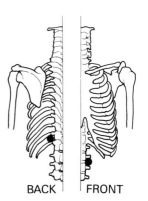

BACK | FRONT

Figure 47

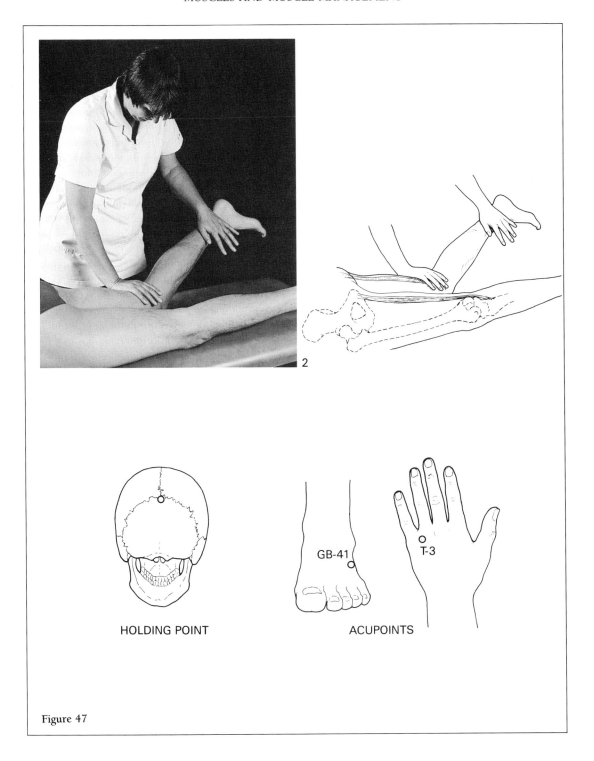

HOLDING POINT

GB-41

T-3

ACUPOINTS

Figure 47

Sports problems

When this muscle is weak it is difficult to bend the knee without bending the hip, too. It can also cause the foot to turn out even though the knees are straight. This muscle is particularly used along with adductors, quadriceps and hamstrings in riding and also in football.

Exercise

Riding, swimming, jogging, skating.

Weights – low leg pulley and abductor machine.

BACK AND OUTSIDE THIGH MUSCLES

Hamstrings

Description

There are three muscles in this group – biceps femoris, semitendinosus and semimembranosus. All three start at the back of the pelvis on the bit of bone that you sit on called the ischial tuberosity. Biceps femoris reaches across the thigh bone and attaches to the shin bone on the outside of the back of the knee, and you can feel the tendons of these muscles at the back of the knee. Basically they hold the back of the hips down towards the knee to stop you flopping forward when you stand, but because they cross two joints (the hip and knee), when you are walking and running they contract at one end, i.e. the knee and expand at the other, i.e. under the buttocks at the same time, so that the contraction goes in a sort of wave down the muscle. This has to be co-ordinated with other muscles and lack of co-ordination is a common cause of injury.

How to test

(*See Figure 48*)

Test position 1
With the athlete lying face down and the leg bent at 60°, stabilize the buttocks with one hand and push the calf down (to straighten the leg). If there is cramping, stabilize by moving your hand down to the middle of the back of the thigh. Don't let the pelvis tilt or the back curve in.

Be sure you are pushing straight down and not sideways if you are testing all three muscles at once. If you push slightly towards the outside as you push down you are testing the medial hamstrings (semi-tendinosus and semimembranosis) and if you push slightly towards the inside as you push down you are testing the lateral hamstring (biceps femoris).

Test position 2
The athlete is standing – which is how most people use this group of muscles! Use the same tests as in (1) whilst the athlete is leaning against a doorpost or wall.

Test position 3
The athlete lies on his or her back, knees raised, feet flat on the table. Stabilize the knee and pull the ankle away from the buttocks.

Other muscles to test if hamstrings are weak: gluteus maximus, gastrocnemius, abdominals, adductors, quadriceps, sartorius, gracilis, tensor fascia lata, latissimus dorsi, pectoralis major clavicular.

HELP

Massage points

1 On the inside of the thigh, go as high as you can and still be on the leg.
2 The lowest part of the hip-bone that you sit on.
3 The most prominent knob on the hip-bone at the back (PSIS at the level of L5). (If you are doing your own points, put your hands on your hips, slide your thumbs back round your waist till you find the knobs at the top of the hips at the back.)

Points to hold

Acupoint S-36 a point 1″ (2.5 cm) below the knee and 1½–2″ (4–5 cm) out in a little dip, together with acupoint LI-11, a point on the outside of the elbow (thumb side) about 2″ (5 cm) round from the point of the elbow and just below the elbow crease.

Diet

This muscle group can be weak if there are problems with constipation, colitis or haemorrhoids, so attention to the type of food the athlete eats is important. Don't let them use laxatives if you possibly can help it. Make the bowel work naturally. I particularly recommend you both read Pritikin's *Diet for Runners* (see Bibliography) and suggest the athlete avoids sugars and refined-starch foods. Foods rich in Vitamin E are good. Hamstrings also react badly to

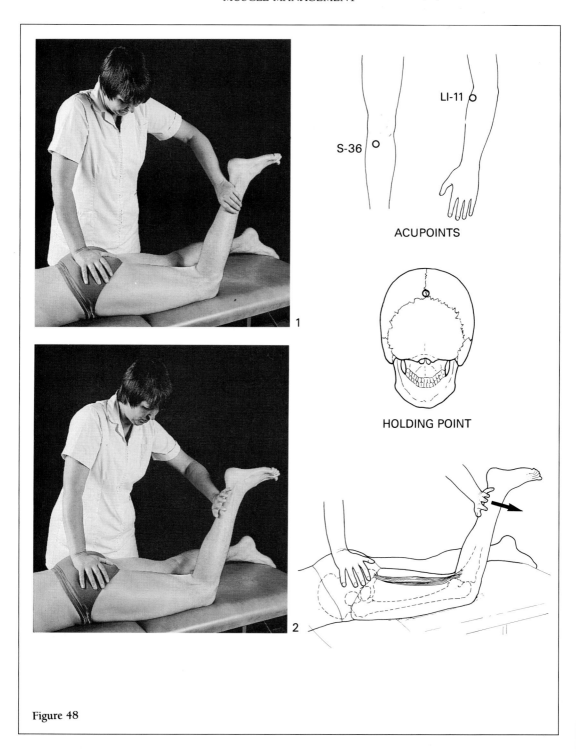

ACUPOINTS

HOLDING POINT

Figure 48

Page 121　　In the top right hand line drawing the arrow should indicate that the pressure is downward and towards the inside.

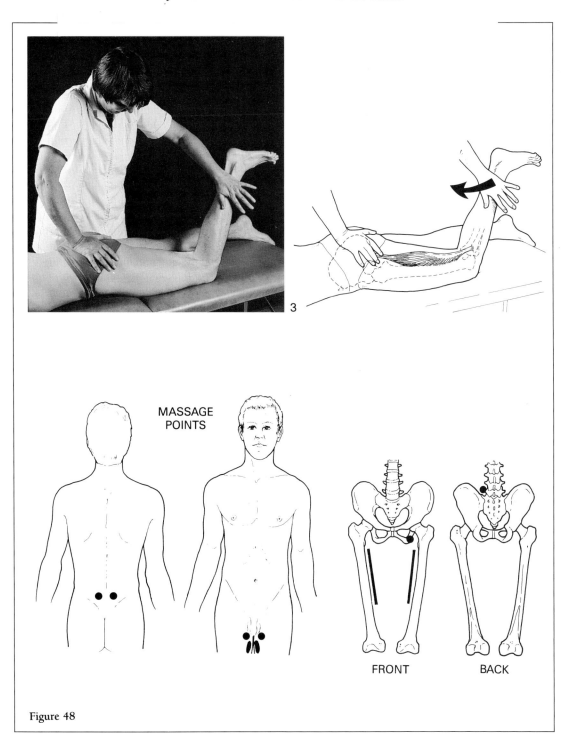

3

MASSAGE POINTS

FRONT　　BACK

Figure 48

dehydration, so make sure the athlete drinks lots of fluid and douses with a sponge during marathons.

Sports problems

Weak hamstrings can cause low back problems, knee problems (knock knees or bow legs), restlessness, fatigue, toxic headache and constipation. Injuries most often occur in running, but almost all sports will stress this muscle in some way – such as kicking a football, karate, rowing, sprinting and hurdling etc. A lot of injuries to this muscle are caused by over-use or cold use followed by interval sprinting, causing the muscle to have poor co-ordination with other muscles. The co-ordination factor is vital and therefore slow and patient retraining in stages is essential, even though it goes against the athlete's competitive nature! If you hurry it, you build trouble for the athlete later. If the athlete is worried about loss of fitness in the meantime, tell them to swim and read Chapter 7 to plan mentally and know their technique to the finest detail.

Don't forget, the advice in this book assumes the athlete has been checked by their physio or doctor for such complications as inflamed bursae and avulsion fractures. If you don't know what these are and the athlete has continuous localized pain, get them to have a check-up.

Pain in the thigh can also be due to sciatic nerve problems. Straight-leg raises causing pain indicates sciatic nerve involvement; bent-leg raises causing pain indicates hamstring problems. Sports that can cause sciatic pain are those which tip the hips one side because of uneven pull, such as rowing (rather than sculling), golf, hurdling, high jump, etc.

Exercise

Running, jumping, skipping, hopping.
Weights – hamstring curls.

Popliteus

Description

This muscle stabilizes the back of the knee and binds or screws the knee-joint together so that it won't bend backwards. It is attached to the lowest part of the thigh bone on the outside and also to the meniscus (the shock-absorbing cartilage between the thigh and shin bones) and then extends across the back of the knee to the tibia (shin bone).

How to test

(*See Figure 49*)

Test position 1
The athlete lies face down and bends the knee at right angles. The foot (and shin) is turned in so that the big toe points across the other leg. Pressure is put on the inside of the big toe and outside of the heel to twist the whole of the shin back straight against the thigh bone. Do not use this test position if there is any foot or ankle injury.

Test position 2
The athlete lies face up, leg bent and dropped out to the side. Stabilize at the ankle (hold it firmly). Pressure is put on the outside of the knee to twist the shin inwards against the thigh. If the popliteus is strong the twist will be felt in the hip muscles instead. This test position is easily confused with sartorius. Here you are trying to twist one part of the leg against the other, whereas with sartorius you are trying to straighten the bent leg.

Other muscles to test if popliteus is weak: sartorius, quadriceps, anterior deltoid, pectoralis major clavicular and sternal.

HELP
Massage points

1 Between the fifth and sixth ribs just under the nipple on the right-hand side of the breastbone.
2 One inch to either side of the spine just below half-way down the length of the shoulder blade at the level of fifth and sixth ribs.

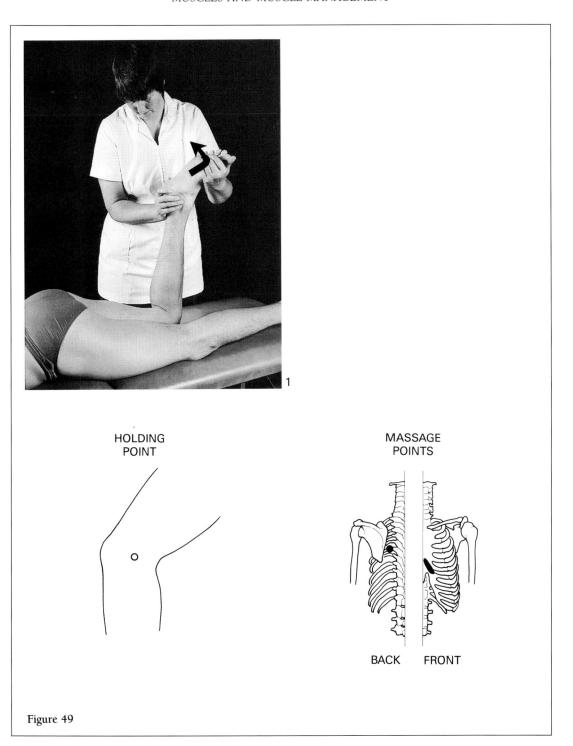

HOLDING
POINT

MASSAGE
POINTS

BACK   FRONT

Figure 49

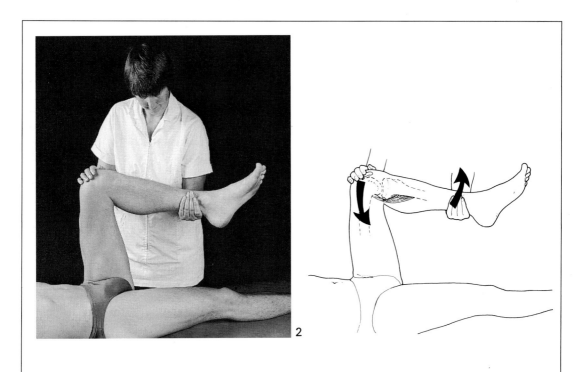

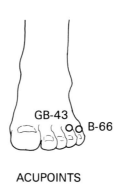

GB-43   B-66

ACUPOINTS

Figure 49

Points to hold

1 The knobs where the collar-bone meets the breastbone at the base of the front neck.
2 (a) Middle of the back of the knee, together with a point on the inside of the leg just below and slightly towards the back of the knee.
(b) The same centre knee spot, together with a point just above the outside of the knee crease.
These inside and outside points are where the muscle begins and ends.
3 Acupoints B-66 and GB-43. B-66 is on the outer edge of the foot at the base of the little toe. Hold it together with GB-43, which is similarly placed at the base of the fourth toe.

Diet

This muscle may go weak with gall-bladder problems such as difficulty in digesting or feeling sleepy after eating fats, jaundice, shingles, one-sided headaches and constipation. This means the athlete should avoid rich, fatty or fried foods and eat foods containing Vitamin A.

Sports problems

Many knee aches can be attributed to this muscle being weak. Typical are hyper-extension (pushing too far back) of the knee and difficult or painful bending of the knee.

Popliteus can also be affected by low neck problems, so sports where both are used frequently are preparatory techniques for shot-putt, tennis serving etc. The knee is particularly prone to tears of cartilage which mostly occur when landing and twisting at the same time or receiving a blow to the side of the knee whilst it is weight bearing as often happens in football and rugby collisions. A strong popliteus will help prevent damage. It is mainly used in swimming, skating and ballet.

Exercise

Walking, running, leg lifts with weights.
Weights – hamstring curl.

Tensor fascia lata

Description

Tensor fascia lata (TFL) runs down the side of the leg (more or less down the seam of your jeans). The main body of the muscle is at the top on the side of the hip above the hip joint itself, then a tendon (the fascia lata or fascia on the outside) runs down to below the knee, stabilizing the outside of both the pelvis and knee joints.

How to test

(*See Figure 50*) The athlete lies on his or her back, the leg is raised 45° and taken out to the side about 30°. The foot is then turned in and pressure is put on the outside of the ankle to press the leg down and in towards the other leg. You will need to stabilize the opposite hip to prevent body rock. Be careful to sort out your test position in your mind first before you pick up the athlete's leg because the leg is heavy to

hold up against gravity at this angle, and the muscle will tire easily before you've even tested it – especially if it's weak.

Other muscles to test if TFL is weak: quadriceps, adductors, gluteus medius and upper part of gluteus maximus, psoas.

HELP

Massage points

1 Along the whole length of the thigh from 1" (2.5 cm) below the kneecap to just above the hip joint.
2 The triangular area at the top back of the hips, 3" (7.5 cm) in towards the spine and up 3" (7.5 cm) (L-2/L-4).

Points to hold

1 The parietal eminence - a point 3" (7.5 cm)

125

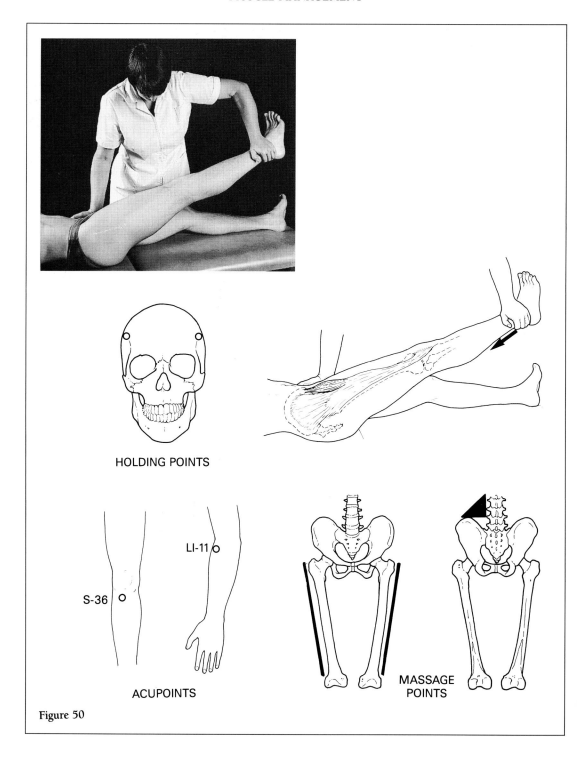

HOLDING POINTS

ACUPOINTS

S-36

LI-11

MASSAGE POINTS

Figure 50

above the ear at the widest point of the head.

2 Acupoint LI-11, which is on the outside of the elbow (thumb side), about 2″ (5 cm) round from the point of the elbow and just below the elbow crease. This should be held together with acupoint S-36, a point below the knee and 1½-2″ (4-5 cm) out (on the fibula) in a little dip.

Diet

This is another muscle that reacts badly to dehydration and weakness can occur if the athlete has constipation (in which case massage the help points from knee to hip), or diarrhoea (in which case massage hip to knee). Generally, they should increase their water intake, eat foods rich in Vitamin B and Vitamin D.

Sports problems

This muscle is not specific to the better known sports except hurdling, waterskiing and tackling in soccer, but is very important in balance together with the gluteus medius (and minimus) in helping with the sideways sway in the middle phase of the walking gait, when taking off from one leg, or when twisting to stop the body giving way to centrifugal force. Weakness may cause low back problems, sciatica, knee problems, bow-leg, constipation, colitis, diarrhoea, menstrual problems and breast soreness.

Exercise

Doing pigeon-toed leg raises when lying on their back, and jogging.

Weights – abductor/adductor machine, leg press and squats.

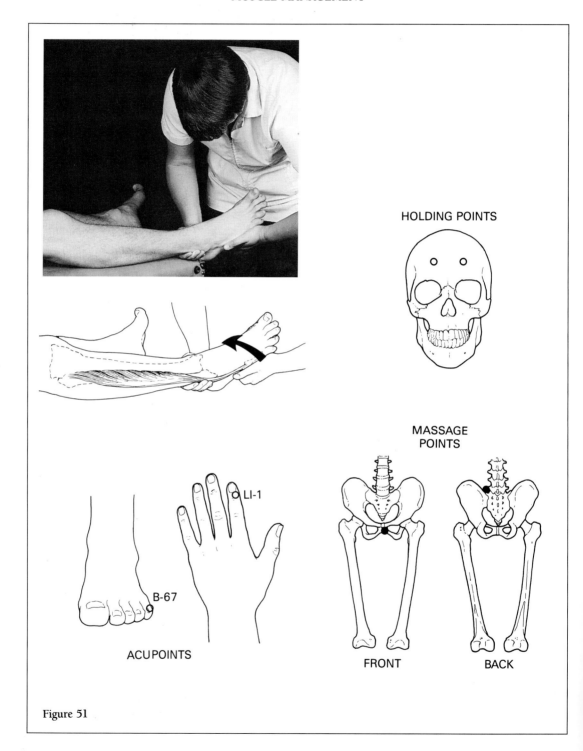

HOLDING POINTS

MASSAGE
POINTS

LI-1

B-67

ACUPOINTS

FRONT   BACK

Figure 51

SHIN, ANKLE AND FOOT MUSCLES

Peroneus

Description

This muscle is found at the outside of the shin towards the back. It raises the foot from the little toe side and so works against both posterior and anterior tibials. The top end is attached in three levels to the fibula (the thin shin bone that makes the outer ankle) as peroneus longus, brevis and tertius and the lower end splits into two, one part attaching to the back of the little toe and the other going under the foot to the base of the big toe (rather like a sling). It gives stability to the outside of the ankle.

How to test

(*See Figure 51*) To test peroneus longus and brevis, get the athlete to point the foot and then push it out to the side as far as they can. Stabilize the foot by holding above the heel on the inside of the foot with one hand, while you pull the foot from the little toe side down and in with the other hand. If you let the foot bend upward towards the head you will then be testing peroneus tertius. If the muscle is weak, the athlete will try everything to use other muscles instead. It is easiest to test the peronei when the athlete's leg is straight, though it is possible to test with the knee bent. Stabilization then becomes more difficult.

Other muscles to test if peroneus is weak: check piriformis, sacrospinalis and popliteus.

HELP
Massage points

1 The tummy button and the upper and lower edges of the pubic bone.
2 The most prominent knobs on the back of the pelvis, at the level of the fifth lumbar vertebrae.

Points to hold

1 The frontal eminence on the forehead, half-way between the eyebrows and hairline above the centre of the eye.
2 The glabella, the innermost edges of the eyebrows just above the inner corners of the eye sockets.
3 Acupoints B-67 and LI-1. B-67 is the nail of the little toe. Hold it and LI-1, which is the nail bed of the index finger.

Diet

Foods that are rich in thiamin and calcium help peroneus. Avoid foods that are high in oxalic acid, particularly at the same meal as you eat calcium-containing foods – so no cream in coffee or on rhubarb, etc.

Sports problems

These muscles are particularly associated with ankle problems, 'weak' ankles that twist easily and 'foot drop'. The ankle, and especially the peroneus, often fails to recover after the first accident and is therefore prone to repeat accidents. It is not infrequent that when the muscle is weak the athlete cannot get into the testing position easily at all. Peronei are very important in maintaining normal foot and ankle function and weakness is often due to one of the small bones of the foot being out of place. To put this right you may need to see a chiropractor or osteopath.

If you twist your ankle at any time – because of an uneven surface whilst running for instance – rub the help points straightaway. They will probably be tender immediately and will help the muscle reset itself and be less traumatized. Peroneus is particularly used in running, swimming, football, cross-country skiing and waterski.

Exercise

Running, jumping, hopping, skipping.
Weights – low leg pulley, quads, knee extensions and sit-ups.

Gastrocnemius

Description

Gastrocnemius and soleus - which lies underneath it - form the main bulk of the calf muscles. They are joined at the achilles tendon, but gastrocnemius reaches across the knee-joint to both sides of the end of the thigh-bone. Both these muscles are very powerful and help you to push the foot down or to stand on your toes by pulling on the achilles tendon. The length of gastrocnemius changes as you bend and straighten the knee by contracting the quadriceps group on the front of the thigh. Gastrocnemius comes into its most advantageous functioning position when the knee is straight and transfers more power to the ankle particularly in running and jumping, whereas soleus is more of an ankle stabilizer, and functions best when the knee is bent.

How to test

(*See Figure 52*) Test this muscle and test soleus to differentiate which of the two is weak.

Test position 1
The athlete stands against a table with hands on the table for balance, then stands on one foot on tiptoe. Pressure is put on the shoulders to pull the athlete down onto flat feet. Repeat with the other foot. This is the easier test position if you are small and the athlete is not. This tests *all* the muscles that point the foot.

Test position 2
The athlete lies face down, leg straight, with the foot pointed. Pressure is put on the ankle to pull it away from the head whilst the ball of the foot is pushed towards the head. You can also stabilize the shin holding underneath as you push on the ball of the foot.

Other muscles to test if gastrocnemius is weak: soleus, sartorius, gracilis, tibialis posterior, peroneus group, toe flexors, pectoralis major clavicular, latissimus dorsi, triceps, adductors, neck flexors and extensors.

HELP

Massage points

1 Two inches (5 cm) above and 1″ (2.5 cm) either side of the navel.
2 Between the tenth, eleventh and twelfth ribs on the back, either side of the spine (these are the bottom three ribs you can feel at the back).

Points to hold

1 The lambda or posterior fontanel. This is the spot on the back of the head where the occipital and two parietal bones of the skull meet and where there is often a whorl in the hair.
2 Acupoints GB-41 and T-3. GB-41 is on the top of the foot where the bones extending back from the fourth and fifth toes join, about half-way from the base of the toes to the ankle. Hold this point with T-3, which is a similar place on the back of the hand.

Diet

Athletes should eat extra Vitamin C. If there is a constant problem, check for allergies, especially to tobacco, low blood sugar or emotional strain or mild shock conditions.

Sports problems

As with soleus, this muscle is used in every sport, especially sprint, long jump, triple jump and ballet, and so it is always helpful to work on the help points. (If they don't need them it will do them no harm!) Gastrocnemius is involved in the gait mechanism which should co-ordinate the various parts of the body as you walk and run. This relationship is particularly vulnerable in sports, because athletes are using their bodies under extreme mental and physical stress. It is always worth turning to Chapter 5, on extra techniques, to check this, as it can relieve a suprising number of problems, especially recurrent ones.

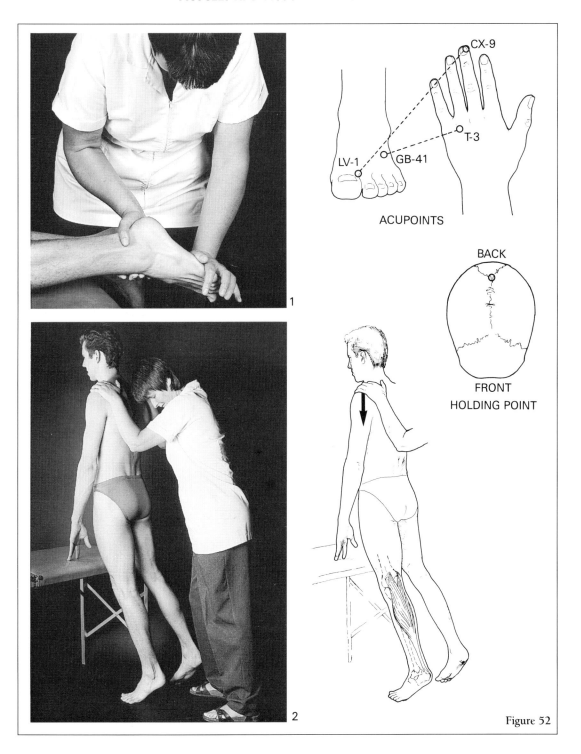

ACUPOINTS

CX-9
T-3
GB-41
LV-1

BACK

FRONT
HOLDING POINT

1

2

Figure 52

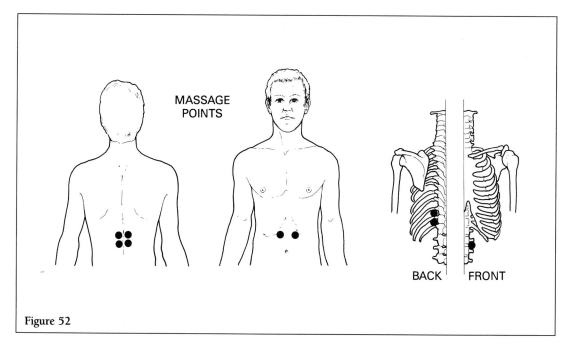

MASSAGE
POINTS

BACK   FRONT

Figure 52

A weak gastrocnemius will cause pain in the calves of the legs, an inability to stand on tiptoe, knee problems and tiredness in the morning.

The most disastrous invention of Man for gastrocnemius is high heels, because constant wearing will lead to a shortening of the achilles tendon and wreck the posture of the upper body by increasing the curve in the low back to compensate to allow you to stand up straight rather than lean forward.

The next most disastrous invention was steep banking around a track. In Ultra marathons, even though track direction was changed every four hours, I could always tell which way the athletes had been running because the fibres of the muscles on the inside kerb leg-side were always quite different to the outside leg, as were hip and shoulder levels and the muscles that support them. Road running where there is a camber has the same effect unless you run out with one foot lower and back with the other lower to compensate. Worn running shoes are equally iniquitous. They may save you money but not injury. Buy first-class quality new ones. Invest in health not injury.

Exercise

Running, jumping, hopping, skipping, walking on tiptoe.

Weights - calf raises, hack squats and squats.

Soleus

Description

This calf muscle points the foot by shortening the achilles tendon at the heel, so it helps gastrocnemius help you to stand on your toes. To stop gastrocnemius helping, you have to bend the knees and then point the foot. It is active as a postural muscle which holds you upright instead of leaning forwards, by stabilizing the shin bones on the heel bone.

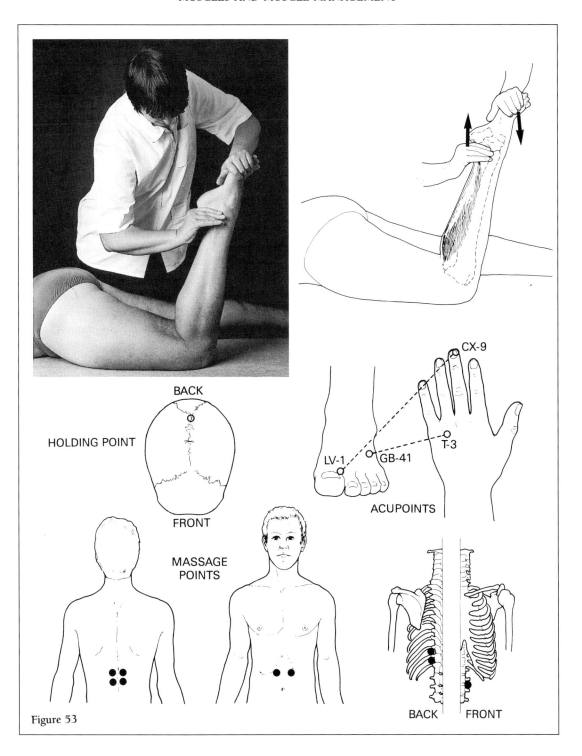

BACK

HOLDING POINT

FRONT

MASSAGE POINTS

CX-9

LV-1 GB-41 T-3

ACUPOINTS

BACK FRONT

Figure 53

How to test

(*See Figure 53*)   The athlete lies face down, the leg is bent at right angles and the foot is pointed. Either pull the heel up and push the ball of the foot down simultaneously or stabilize the front of the ankle as you push down on the ball of the foot. If the foot twists at all the athlete is trying to use posterior tibials, toe flexors and peroneus muscles.

Other muscles to test if soleus is weak: gastrocnemius, sartorius, gracilis, latissimus dorsi, adductors, triceps, peroneus, flexor hallucis longus, toe flexors, pectoralis major clavicular, neck flexors and extensors.

HELP

Massage points

1 One inch (2.5 cm) out and 2″ (5 cm) up either side of the belly button.
2 On the back, either side of the spine at the level of the last two ribs (T-11 and 12).

Points to hold

1 The posterior fontanel or lambda - the spot on the back of the head, here the occipital and the two parietal bones of the skull meet.
2 Acupoints GB-41 and T-3. GB-41 is on the top of the foot where the bones extending back from the fourth and fifth toes join, about half-way from the base of the toes to the ankle. Hold this point at the same time as T-3, which is found in a similar place on the back of the hand.

3 Acupoints LV-1 and CX-9. Hold the point LV-1, on the nail bed of the big toe nearest the other toes, together with point CX-9 on the middle finger-nail bed.

Diet

Foods rich in vitamin C will help soleus. This muscle also typically goes weak if the athlete is allergic or smokes.

Sports problems

Soleus is used anywhere you need to point your toes, stand on tiptoe or spring from a standing start especially gymnastics, rugby, netball, basketball, volley-ball, racket sports and sprint starts. Because of its association with the adrenal glands it is important to check this muscle where there is any form of allergy asthma, low blood sugar, exercise fatigue or stress. It can also react badly to emotional strain and mild shock conditions following accidents, or trauma following heavy outpouring of adrenalin and a lot of excitement.

The athlete will complain of aching calves, especially after having been on his/her feet for a long time, which is not due to calcium deficiency (which also causes tightness). A weak soleus will cause a forward-leaning posture. Read the pages about gastrocnemius. These muscles work so closely together that almost everything there is relevant to soleus, too.

Exercise

Running, jumping, hopping, skipping.
Weights - calf raises, hack squats, squats.

Anterior tibial

Description

This is a shin muscle. It pulls the big-toe side of the foot upwards towards the head. It also stabilizes the inside of the ankle and controls swaying when you stand.

How to test

(*See Figure 54*)   Test with the leg straight and the toes and ankle flexed so that the toes pull up towards the knee. Pressure is put against the foot to push the toes down away from the knee. You may need to stabilize the leg above the knee to stop it twisting.

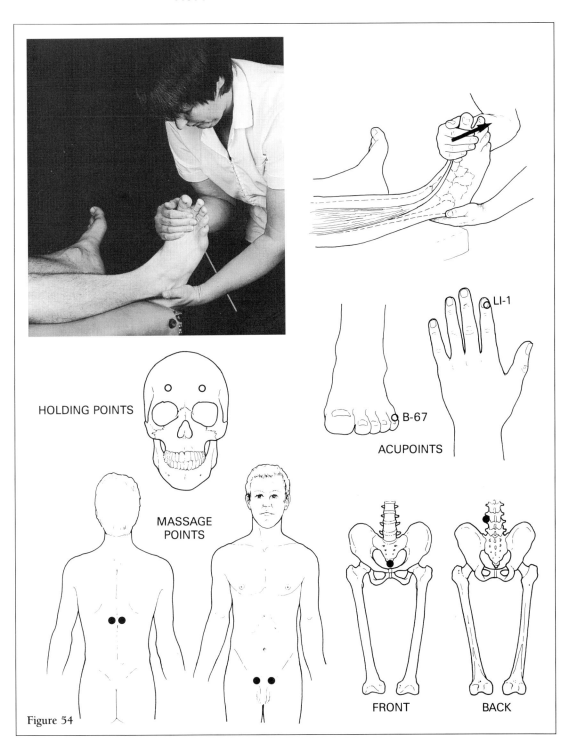

HOLDING POINTS

LI-1

B-67

ACUPOINTS

MASSAGE POINTS

FRONT   BACK

Figure 54

135

Other muscles to test if anterior tibials are weak: peroneus, psoas, sacrospinalis.

HELP
Massage points

1 About ¾″ (2 cm) above the pubic bone, just either side of the centre.
2 The upper edge of the second lumbar vertebrae, 1″ (2.5 cm) either side of the spine.

Points to hold

1 The frontal eminences – the bumps on the forehead half-way between the centre of the eye and the hairline.
2 Acupoints B-67 and LI-1 – the outside of the nail of the little toe, together with the outer edge of the nail of the index finger.

Diet

Consistently weak anterior tibials can be an indicator of, or can be affected by, bladder problems. Foods rich in Vitamin A will help this muscle.

Sports problems

Anterior tibials are used especially in hill walking, mountaineering, racing, sailing and running. The most common injury to this muscle is tripping up over something, especially when in full flight of running, and so can occur in any sport where running is involved. It can also be injured if you tie your laces too tightly or plant your foot too hard in bowling at cricket. A constantly weak muscle is usually present in flat-footedness or fallen arches. 'Shin splints' and bunions are often associated with the anterior tibial. It cannot protect itself and so gets very fatigued especially in long-distance walking and ice-skating.

Anterior tibial can be responsible for 'foot drop' problems, especially when reactive to eye muscles. This is when the muscles test strong but the athlete continually trips over things for no apparent reason. If you suspect this problem, turn to Chapter 6 and use the reactive muscles technique, together with the eye muscles.

Exercise

Walking on the outside of the foot.
Weights – quads knee extensions, sit-ups, low leg pulley.

Posterior tibial

Description

This muscle stabilizes the inner ankle joint. It runs from the back of the fibula (the thin bone on the outside of the shin) and also the back of the tibia (shin bone), down the back of the shin and pulls the foot bones down from the underside, twisting the foot inwards slightly as it does so. It also helps to point the toes by pointing the foot.

How to test

(*See Figure 55*) Test with the foot turned down (pointed) and in as far as possible. pressure is put on the ball of the foot to push it up and outwards. Stabilize the back of the ankle as you do so or the athlete will try to use gracilis to help.

Other muscles to test if posterior tibials are weak: gracilis, popliteus, psoas, peroneus, anterior tibials, toe and foot flexors, soleus, gastrocnemius.

HELP
Massage points

1 One inch (2.5 cm) out either side from the tummy button and 2″ (5 cm) up towards the head.
2 The upper edge of the second lumbar vertebrae, 1″ (2.5 cm) either side of the spine. Find the most prominent knobs on the back of the hips (level of fifth lumbar) and count up three bumps on the spine to get to the second lumbar.

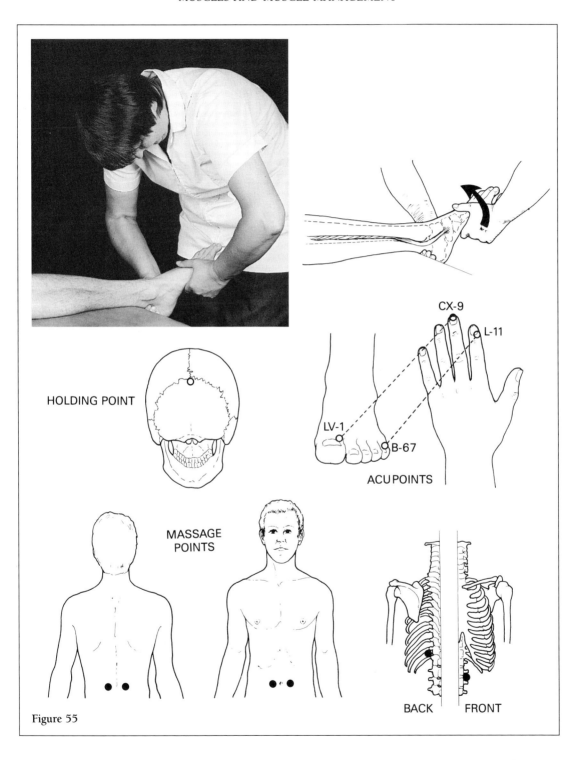

CX-9

L-11

HOLDING POINT

LV-1

B-67

ACU POINTS

MASSAGE
POINTS

BACK   FRONT

Figure 55

Points to hold

1 The frontal eminences – these are points on either side of the forehead, midway between the centre of each eye and the hairline.
2 The lambda – the point on the back of the head head where the occipital and parietal bones meet. There is often a whorl in the hair here.
3 Acupoints B-67 and LI-1 – the outside of the nail of the little toe and the outer edge of the nail of the index finger at the same time.
4 Acupoints LV-1 and CX-9. Hold the point LV-1, on the nail bed of the big toe nearest the other toes, together with point CX-9 on the middle finger-nail.

Diet

Weakened shin muscles, especially the tibialis group (of which this is one), are often indicators of bladder problems. This muscle can be upset by a lack of Vitamin E and drained adrenals. So reduce your stress levels (see Chapter 7).

Sports problems

This muscle is involved in raising the longitudinal arch of the foot (heel to big toe) and so is often weak with flat feet, or foot pronation. Suspect this also if the athlete's wet footprint does not show a little toe image.

This muscle works with the other toe and calf muscles to push off, so is important for a good start out of the blocks and in all jumping sports. It gives 'spring' to the foot and works against the peroneus group of muscles to balance the athlete on take off.

If posterior tibials are weak this can cause foot pronation, fallen arches, inability to stand on your toes, limping.

Exercise

Running, jumping, hopping, skipping, walking on your toes.

THE MUSCLES OF THE FOOT

Description

As with the hands, there are many muscles that control the foot and here I have chosen only the simplest.

The toe extensors

Do not be confused by the fact that the long toe extensors curl the toes up (especially the big toe) but also assist in flexing the ankle. This is because they cross several joints running between the shin bones and the ends of the toes. Their action is also helped by shorter extensor muscles.

How to test the big toe

(*See Figure 56a*)   The athlete sits, feet flat on the floor, with the ankle in a neutral position (neither bent nor straightened), then lifts up the big toe. Holding the ankle round the back of the heel to stabilize it, put pressure on the nail of the big toe to push it back down to the floor. There should be no movement of the ankle. When both short and long extensors are weak, the athlete cannot lift the big toe.

HELP

Massage points

1 Behind the nipple on the chest wall between the fourth and fifth ribs.
2 Just below the bottom points of the shoulder blades between the eighth and ninth ribs.

Points to hold

The lambdoidal suture. Find the top centre of the back of the neck. Go up and diagonally outward from there, each side, for about 2½″ (6-7 cm) on the skull.

How to test the other toes

(*See Figure 56b*)   If you are testing the toes without the big toe, the test position is similar, but here the athlete raises the toes off the ground whilst you contact the back of the toes to push them to the floor.

HELP
Massage points

1 On the top outer edges of the front of the pubic bone.
2 The most prominent bumps on the back of the top of the hips (L-5-PSIS).

Points to hold

1 Anterior fontanel or bregma – the spot just back from the centre top of the head, where the frontal and two parietal (side) bones of the skull join.
2 Acupoints GB-41 and T-3. GB-41 is on the top of the foot, half-way between the base of the fourth toe and the ankle. Hold it at the same time as T-3, similarly placed on the back of the hand between the base of the ring finger and the wrist crease.

Sports problems

Toe extensors are used in all running sports.

Exercise

Weights – low leg pulley, floor ankle exercises.

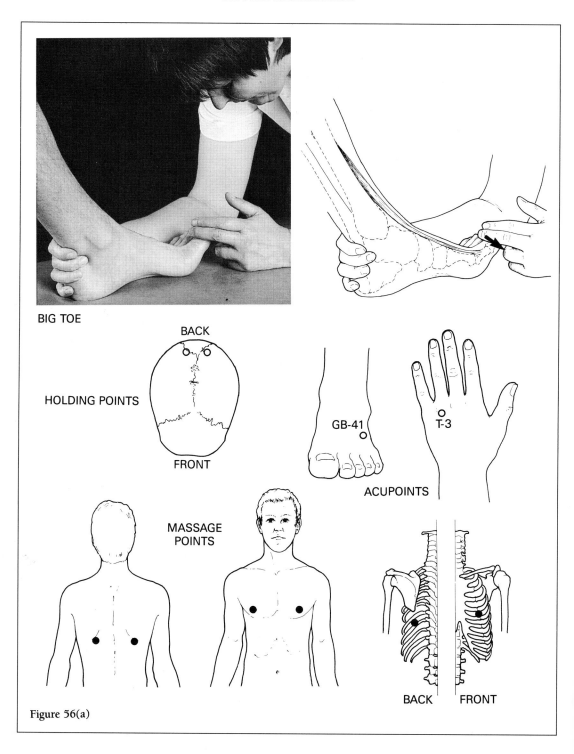

BIG TOE

HOLDING POINTS

BACK

FRONT

MASSAGE
POINTS

GB-41

T-3

ACUPOINTS

BACK   FRONT

Figure 56(a)

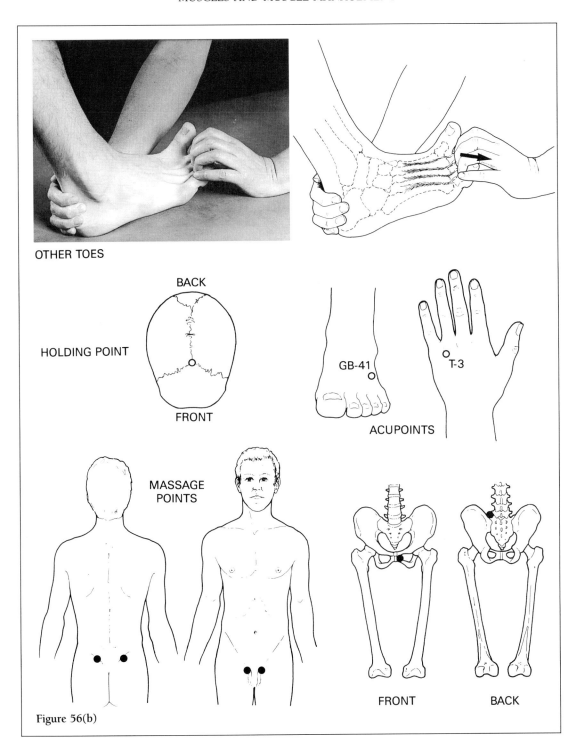

OTHER TOES

HOLDING POINT

BACK

FRONT

GB-41

T-3

ACUPOINTS

MASSAGE POINTS

FRONT

BACK

Figure 56(b)

The toe flexors

Description

The big toe flexor goes across several joints, running from the outside of the shin round behind the ankle and along under the foot to the end of the big toe - so it can also help in pointing the foot, especially for ballet dancers. Whilst bending the big toe down towards the sole of the foot it also stabilizes the inside of the ankle.

How to test the big toe

(*See Figure 57a*) The athlete holds the ankle in a neutral position (not bent up or down) and curls the tip of the big toe down. Pressure is put on the underneath of the big toe to straighten it, whilst at the same time you support the joint between the big toe and the foot.

The other toes

The muscles here are the lumbricals and flexor digitorum brevis. These muscles work together to curl the toes down from the first and second joints.

How to test the other toes

(*See Figure 57b*) The athlete's foot is stabilized close to the toes. The athlete pulls the toes down. Pressure

is put under the first bone (lumbricals) or middle bone (flexor digitorum brevis) to straighten them.

HELP FOR ALL TOE FLEXORS
Massage points

1 On the upper outer edges of the pubic bone.
2 Inside the most prominent knobs on the top back of the hips (L-5-PSIS).

Points to hold

1 Frontal eminences - either side of the forehead, between the centre of the eyebrows and the hairline.
2 Acupoints - same as toe extensors (*see Figure 56b*).

Sports problems

Toe flexors are used in ballet, sprint start and running, high jump, beam (gym), hill walking.

Exercise

Weights - hack squats and calf raises.

Abductor Hallucis

Description

This muscle when weak often leads to bunion formation, flat foot (fallen arches) and consequent knee problems. This all happens when the big toe cannot be pulled straight to balance the foot and support the arch. Recurrent problems may need a podiatrist's help.

How to test

(*See Figure 58*) With the athlete's foot in a neutral position (neither held up nor pointing down), stabil-

ize it by holding the foot on the little toe side. The athlete spreads the toes, especially the big toe, then pressure is put on the side of the big toe, to push it back in towards the other toes.

HELP
Massage points

On the left side of the chest wall, between the seventh and eighth ribs on the left of the back next to the spine, level with, but inside the bottom of the shoulder-blade.

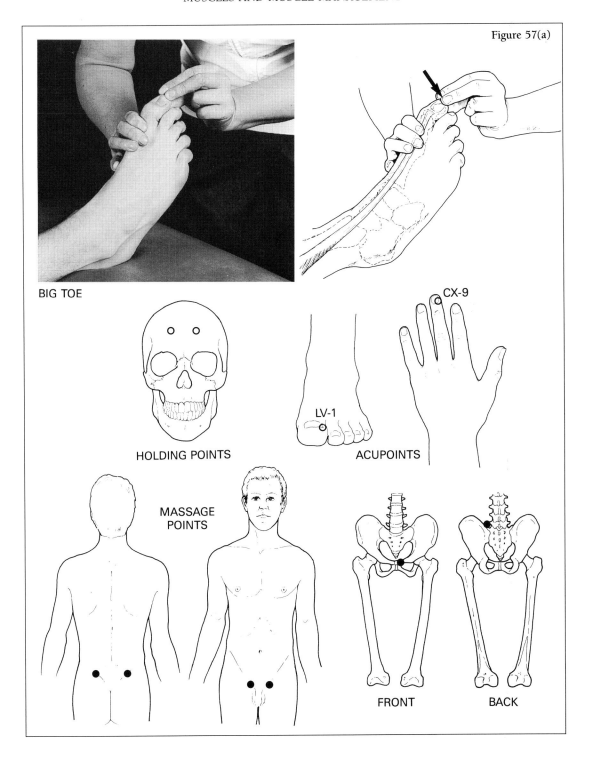

Figure 57(a)

BIG TOE

HOLDING POINTS

CX-9

LV-1

ACUPOINTS

MASSAGE POINTS

FRONT   BACK

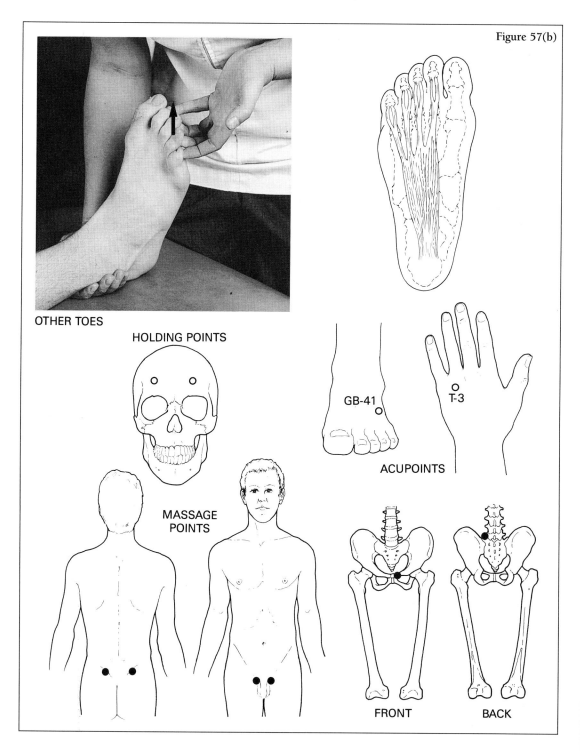

Figure 57(b)

OTHER TOES

HOLDING POINTS

MASSAGE POINTS

GB-41

T-3

ACUPOINTS

FRONT

BACK

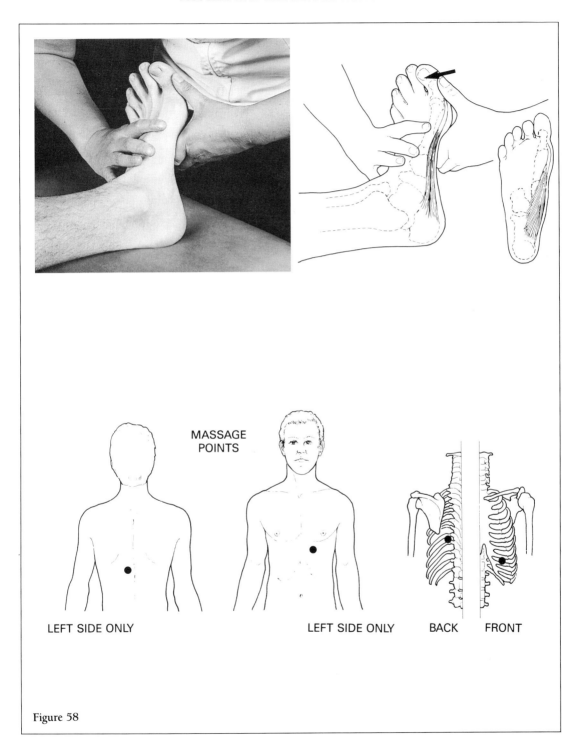

MASSAGE
POINTS

LEFT SIDE ONLY   LEFT SIDE ONLY   BACK   FRONT

Figure 58

Points to hold

Half an inch (1.2 cm) above the posterior fontanel or lambda - the spot on the back of the head, where the occipital and the two parietal bones of the skull meet.

General pain reduction formula

This is a useful formula which will reduce general pain levels and may even deal with the problem altogether. It follows the Chinese Acupuncture Meridian cycle. If you don't know what this is, don't worry - it will work anyway.

Assess the pain level on a score of 0-10. Test and correct the list of muscles below one after the other. If a muscle will not strengthen, leave it and move on to the next. Retest it at the end, as it may then be strong. If it isn't, then turn to Chapter 6 for more help with extra techniques.

1 *Muscle test order:*
    supraspinatus
    teres major
    pectoralis major clavicular
    latissimus dorsi
    subscapularis
    quadriceps (general test)
    peroneus
    psoas
    gluteus medius
    teres minor
    popliteus or anterior deltoid
    pectoralis major sternal
    anterior serratus
    tensor fascia lata

2 Follow this by checking:
    (a) auricular and visual inhibition, and
    (b) either Emotional Stress Relief (ESR) plus Trauma, or Pain Chasing II (see Extra Techniques in Chapter 6).

3 Retest any muscles that didn't strengthen before.

4 Reassess the pain level.

Very often, doing only these techniques will solve the problem.

CHAPTER 5

Putting it all together and going for the top

So far in this book I have told you how to test for weak muscles and ways of strengthening them. You will find these methods work most of the time. However, it is rare to find only one weak muscle, so you are then faced with a decision: either strengthen as you go, or find all the weak muscles first and see the complete picture before you start to strengthen.

The first method works well and is uncomplicated, but it is slow and does not show you any relationships between muscles weaknesses. The second method requires more sophistication and is faster and more efficient.

The body's prime concern is survival and where it cannot solve a problem and function as required because of injury, it will find a way round by using other muscles (the synergists), compensating as it does so. This stresses the synergists which then may fail and in turn cause further compensation to be made – in a sort of domino effect. For this reason the pain the athlete feels may be due to an over-worked compensatory muscle (the synergists) rather than the problem itself. (Often an athlete will mistakenly 'run through the pain' and it goes away. This is because the shout for help that the pain was signalling has gone unheeded, so the body has now compensated by using other muscles.)

If you then only treat the compensation and not the cause, the problem will re-occur again and again. The body has an innate knowledge and a preferred order of weaknesses being put right too, that may not appear logical to us. Trust it.

How to know what to treat first

1 Test all the muscles you feel are relevant to the problem and make a note of the weak ones.
2 Retest the weak muscles you found whilst either you or the athlete hold one hand in the priority hand-mode – this is where you place the tip of the middle finger against the middle-joint crease on the inside of the thumb. Any weak muscle that now becomes strong is priority. Fix it first. If you find more than one priority then the athlete is probably dehydrated. Have them drink a large glass of water and retest. Or, it's fine to fix all the priority muscles as the order is not significant – but this is rare. Rather, suspect your testing.

How to decide which aspect to fix first

Frequently a muscle will require several ways of strengthening to be really firm and stay strong for longer, and it is always a good idea to back it up with the appropriate nutritional support.

Retest the weak muscle using the SNEAK test – this is a series of hand-modes. Either you or the athlete holds:

(a) Thumb tip to index-finger tip = Structural problem
(b) Thumb tip to middle-finger tip = Nutritional problem
(c) Thumb tip to ring-finger tip = Emotional problem
(d) Thumb tip to little-finger tip = Acupuncture problem

If the muscle now becomes strong when tested with the hand-mode it needs help in that particular hand-mode's aspect. For structural problems work on the help points to rub. Use the hold points on the head only, or anything relevant in Chapter 6 on extra muscle techniques or mechanics.

For nutritional problems, chew a small piece of one or more of the foods suggested and see if the muscle becomes strong.

For emotional problems, turn to Chapter 7 and use the emotional stress release (ESR) techniques.

For acupuncture, use the acupoints. Often more than one of these hand-modes will make the muscle strong. When you have fixed the priority muscle you may find some or all of the others that were weak are now strong. They were part of the body's compensation and adaptation mechanism.

Hidden weaknesses

If you suspect a muscle is only a 51 per cent strong muscle, pinch or slap the athlete gently at the same time as you test. If it becomes weak again, it needs more work or some other therapy. Retest with the SNEAK test. You have probably missed something.

If you are not sure you have done enough on the help points, touch them and retest the muscle again and see if there is a change in strength. If it shows no change, you have done enough. If it becomes stronger, do more. If it goes weak again, do something else. Optimal times for massage points is 30 seconds' firm rubbing. More than that does no good and only bruises. Holding points may need any time between ten seconds and ten minutes, but again the average is 30 seconds. When you are experienced you can feel when the point is finished, either because you or the athlete sighs or you feel suddenly more relaxed and the pulses are slow and even.

Aerobic/anaerobic

Sports often involve repetitive use of a muscle which, although it tests as strong, becomes fatigued after sustained or repeated action.

1 Test the suspect muscle. It will be strong.
2 Retest at least ten times quickly - the muscle becomes weak.

3 If it now becomes and remains strong when the athlete holds the massage or holding points, these points need working on for at least 3-4 minutes as there has been inadequate lymphatic clearing and an oxygen debt in the muscle, causing clogging and thus weakening.

Surrogate testing

There are times when you would like to but cannot test muscles. Such times are when the athlete is exhausted, unconscious, dehydrated or in a wheelchair and so cannot get into a convenient testing position or cannot understand what you say because of hearing problems or a language barrier. It is under such circumstances that you might use a surrogate.

A surrogate is someone else, preferably of the same family and of the same sex, who is muscle tested whilst in contact with the athlete by touching the athlete at the same time as being tested. It goes without saying that the surrogate's muscles must test strong first! So proceed as follows:

1 Test the surrogate and correct any muscle weaknesses.
2 Retest the surrogate while s/he is in physical contact with the athlete. The surrogate breaks contact if weakness is found.
3 Do any help points necessary on the athlete, *not* on the surrogate (unless there is no other way).

4 Retest the surrogate who is once more in contact with the athlete. If you have done the corrections well the surrogate will now test strong, which means the athlete will be strong. I have known dramatic changes occur in the space of a few minutes with this method.

Switching

Just occasionally muscle weaknesses show up on the wrong side of the body – right instead of left, upper body instead of lower, or front instead of back or vice versa. For this reason it is recommended that you work on the help points on both sides of the body even though the problem only shows on one side.

Switching place usually occurs as a response to a stress of some sort. This can be mental, physical or chemical. A typical time would be after a road traffic accident, after eating an allergen, after being carsick, etc. The body gets its messages mixed. Test for this by finding a strong muscle and then retest fast three times, using your right hand, left hand and then right hand to test. If the muscle weakens now, then switching is happening. If you suspect this might be

a problem for yourself or the athlete, rub the following points together before you test.

(a) *Right to left switching* – massage belly button and K-27 (K-27 is just underneath the collar bone either side of the top of the breastbone).
(b) *Top to bottom switching* – massage belly button at the same time as CV-24 and GV-27 (CV-24 and GV-27 are on the bottom and top lips directly under the nose).
(c) *Front to back switching* – massage belly button and coccyx (tail bone).

Massage the athlete's points. They will come to no harm if you massage the points when there is no problem, so why not do them anyway?

Anti-cramp

Just occasionally when you are testing a muscle – hamstrings or soleus for example – the muscle goes into cramp. Traditional methods have been to forcibly stretch the muscle and/or massage it deeply. A far easier, quicker and less painful method is to brush

it very vigorously and very *lightly* for ten seconds as though brushing powder off it. This disperses the excess energy stored in the muscle and it will return to normal. This is an excellent first-aid technique and also useful if one wakes in the night with cramp.

Origin and insertion and spindle cell techniques

There is one technique that almost always works, but because of this I tend to use it as a last resort, as the effect can be short-lived.

Working on the sensory cells in the muscle itself, there are two ways of strengthening a muscle. The first is to push the two ends of the muscle (the origin

and insertion) together. This has the general effect of shortening the muscle artificially and thus strengthening it. (The reverse is true also – if you pull the two ends of a strong muscle apart it will test weak.)

The second is to pull apart the 'spindle cells' in the belly of the muscle so that they are not overcrowded and can work more efficiently. This will strengthen the muscle. Naturally, the reverse is true also – if you push the belly of the muscle together it will weaken the muscle.

These effects can be dramatically demonstrated on the large postural muscles such as quadriceps. However, if you have not sorted out the underlying problem in the muscle, such techniques will not last long and the muscle will reset itself to accommodate the old problem within a very short time. I use it when working on reactive muscles (see Chapter 6) or to get an athlete through a difficulty until I can work on the underlying problem.

CHAPTER 6
Advanced techniques

Reactive muscle technique

If, when you have worked on all the usual help points, there is still a problem – still pain, spasm, twinges or stiffness; the posture looks distorted but the muscles test strong; restricted range of movement, over-enlarged, very flabby muscles; persistent recruiting of muscles that have a similar action, or you don't know what else to do to help – try the reactive muscle technique.

There appear to be some common combinations, although any muscle can be reactive to any other muscle. The problem seems to be one of synchronization, which becomes disturbed through injury or over-use of that particular combination of muscles. The result is that one muscle does not become inhibited normally (switch off properly) or at the right time to allow its antagonist (opposite muscle) to contract, so it has to work at half strength.

This may lead to stabbing pain in the muscle that cannot relax or an ache in the overworked antagonist, or even group of antagonists. Other symptoms can be spasm, malfunction, joints that seem to give way suddenly or a muscle that is strong on testing and yet gives pain when you use it.

Frequently posture can be a clue to finding the muscle that won't relax and is 'set too high'. Observe the athlete closely for postural problems such as ears, shoulders, hips, knees or feet not level or twisted forward or back. Muscles move bones and hold bones in place, so work out from what you see and from Figure 1 which muscles are likely to be too tight. For instance, a high shoulder on one side can indicate a tight upper trapezius on that side, drawing the

shoulder up, or a tight latissimus dorsi on the other side pulling that shoulder down.

The most common way of finding a muscle set too high is to test two muscles together. If both were strong previously and now one is weak, then the strong one is set too high and is inhibiting other muscles when it shouldn't. Typical of this would be upper trapezius and latissimus dorsi.

Another way of finding reactive muscles is to test two muscles in quick succession: test muscle A (strong), now test muscle B (strong); retest muscle A (now weak).

How to correct reactive muscles

1 Find the muscle set too high. (This is the one that remains strong.)
2 Find the muscle that goes weak (there may be more than one) by either of the methods described above, whilst the athlete holds the bridge of his or her nose.
3 Switch off the strong muscle by any or all of the following:
   (a) pulling the ends of the muscle apart;
   (b) pinching the belly of the muscle together (this is usually very tender);
   (c) stroking the muscle very lightly and very vigorously;
   (d) stroking the massage points very lightly;
   (e) smartly tap the points to hold (not the acupoints). Notice that this is the opposite of normal instructions as given in Chapter 3. Of all

the available help points it is best to work on the muscle itself, (a–c above).

4 Retest the muscle(s) that was (were) weak; they should now be strong. If they aren't, strengthen them. Retest the previously weak muscles several times to reset them.

5 Tap on the athlete's forehead in a 2″ (5 cm) clockwise circle. This will reset the once strong muscle that you weakened back to normal (if it hasn't already reset itself).

6 Test all the combinations of muscles in the way you first tried and if you have done the technique correctly all the muscles should be strong with no pain or ache. If not, repeat the correction.

A surprising but not unusual combination is eye muscles and ankle muscles. Symptomatic behaviour includes tripping over kerbstones, stumbling and lack of confidence in going downstairs or steep inclines. What happens is that the victim's ankle muscles switch off whenever s/he looks down – an unfortunate state of affairs for any athlete!

How to test and correct

The athlete lies on his or her back and moves their eyes up and down. If the feet seem to be following the eye movement involuntarily then correction is needed. Have the athlete look straight ahead or upwards and test anterior and posterior tibials and peroneus. Ask the athlete to look down towards the feet (the neck muscles may also be involved here, too) and retest anterior and posterior tibials and peroneus. If any now test weak, this confirms the problem.

To reset the balance, temporarily weaken the eye muscles by pressing firmly on the spot which is in a small hollow 2″ (5 cm) up, 45° diagonally from the ear towards the centre back of the head – on a level with the highest point on the eyebrows. Immediately strengthen the muscles that were weak using the relevant 'help' points whilst the athlete looks down towards the feet. The eye muscles will reset themselves quite quickly on retesting as at first.

If the testing brings to mind a particularly nasty fall or collision that involved falling whilst looking down, work on it using emotional stress relief (ESR) techniques (see Chapter 7).

Pain chasing

There are many ways of reducing pain apart from taking pain-killers. Several methods are used in acupuncture and another method uses trigger points. In this book I am recommending two which, as far as I know, do not come from either of these sources.

The first method works on the muscle itself and is for acute pain. The second uses the imagination and is useful for residual pain.

Pain chasing I

1 Find out by muscle testing exactly which muscle is at fault. It's usually weak but may test strong and perhaps slightly juddery in feel.

2 Look at the picture of the muscle and compare the picture with the athlete.

3 Find another muscle that is strong to act as an indicator muscle.

4 Carefully and slowly – bit by bit – feel the muscle that hurts and, as you do so, retest the indicator muscle. The point you touch when the indicator muscle goes weak is where the problem is to be found. (This method does not tell you what the problem is, however, only that there is a problem.)

5 Firmly pinch together either side of the spot on the painful muscle that caused the indicator muscle to weaken.

6 If you have been successful, touching the spot will now not cause the indicator muscle to weaken.

7 Check the rest of the muscle and treat if necessary. A typical muscle frequently found with this kind of problem is upper trapezius.

8 Tap in a 2″ (5 cm) diameter clockwise circle on the athlete's forehead to reset the muscle-mind connection and ask the athlete where they now feel pain (if any).

9 Go back to stage 1 above and chase the pain from the new muscle. This often unravels old compensation chains the body has built up to try to solve a problem itself.

Pain chasing II

1 The athlete should sit (or lie) in a comfortable position.
2 Activate the pain by muscle testing or positioning the body so that the pain re-occurs. Assess the pain level on a scale of 1–10.
3 Encourage the athlete to describe the pain *as exactly as possible* – ask questions such as: What is the exact area of the pain in inches or centimetres? What shape is it? Does it have a colour? Does it have a consistency, such as hard like stone, or solid like a block of wood or metal, or soft like a cloud? Is it moving or static? Gyrating, spreading, shooting, throbbing? and so on. In-vent questions to keep the athlete's attention on the pain.
4 Ask the athlete to keep breathing deeply and watching the pain – 'breathe through the pain' is a helpful phrase.
5 After about a minute ask the athlete to describe the pain again in detail; ask questions like: Is it still red or green (or whatever it was)? Is it still 2″ by 2″ (or whatever size was originally mentioned), nebulous and gyrating? etc. Usually it has changed in some degree and has lessened.
6 Reassess the pain level and repeat stages 3–5 till the pain has evaporated. When it has gone instruct the athlete not to look for the pain again, as they have no need of it any longer.

Stretch and spray, fascial release

These are first-aid methods sometimes used in physiotherapy and Rolfing but which are worth mentioning here. They work on the muscle itself.

How to recognize this problem

A muscle that is strong will contract just as strongly from a stretched position as from a neutral position. If the muscle nerve receptors become confused, the muscle will weaken after stretching.

1 Test the muscle – it should be strong even though it appears to malfunction in some way.
2 Put the muscle at full stretch. The athlete then holds this position while you give it a *gentle* pull to stretch it even more.
3 If the muscle now becomes weak on retesting, correct with stretch and spray, fascial release or hyperton X (see below).

Stretch and spray

Put the muscle into a stretched position and spray it with PR (pain-relieving) spray for 30 seconds. This spray contains fluromethane which will freeze the area. (It is easily available from the chemist.) Hold the can about 18″ (45 cm) away. A slight frosting on the skin will be sufficient – don't overdo it and give the athlete frost-bite! Alternatively, an ice cube wrapped in a handkerchief will do, though it is rather messy.

Work only from the origin of the muscle (the end on the bone that does not move when you contract the muscle) to the insertion (the end attached to the bone that does move when you contract the muscle). Spray or rub with the ice cube in this one direction only for about 30 seconds, maintaining the muscle stretch. Retest the muscle as before. It should now stay strong.

Fascial release

1 Find the muscle that needs assistance (see above).
2 Cover the area with a dusting of talcum powder or massage oil to prevent skin burn.
3 Stretch the fascia of the muscle (the covering of the muscle which has become too tight like a

sausage skin). Gradually increasing the pressure, work until you are using deep pressure (one thumb on top of the other) down the muscle (from origin to insertion) in line with the muscle fibres – do this between two and five times. Never work across the fibres.

Strain–counter-strain

Often when an injury heals the muscle receptors do not get the message that all is now well, and they continue to protect the body as though it were still injured.

How to test

1 Choose a muscle which is strong, but which still has a pain spot or is in a general area of pain.
2 The athlete contracts the muscle and pressure is then applied to contract it even more.
3 Retest the muscle normally. If strain–counter-strain technique is needed the muscle will now be weak.

How to correct weakness with strain–counter-strain

1 Find the most tender spot in the muscle – this can be in the muscle belly or tendon. Hold the spot.
2 As the athlete breathes out slowly, the athlete's

4 Retest as before – the muscle should now stay strong. Typically, pectoralis minor needs this treatment in athletes who are round-shouldered or who frequently sleep with their arms behind or above their head, indicating a lymph drainage problem.

body is moved so that the two ends of the muscle are as close together as possible (and the muscle is therefore very contracted) and the same pain spot will have gone or almost gone. For example, if the affected muscle is on the front of the body, contract the body by bending forward; if it is on the back of the body stretch the body backward. The nearer the location of the affected muscle to the side of the body the more you will have to twist the body.
3 The athlete then holds this position, whilst two-handed or two-fingered pressure is put upon the sore spot in the belly for the muscle to pull it apart continuously for 30 seconds. If the sore spot is on the tendon at either end, then pressure is put on the point to push it towards the centre (belly) of the muscle for 90 seconds.
4 *Very slowly*, bring the body back to a normal position. The athlete *must* remain entirely passive and provide no help whatsoever to lift or move a limb.

Nutritional assistance to help the muscles can be found in foods containing Vitamin B_{12}.

Hyperton X

This technique (a combination drawn from other methods and put together by Frank Mahoney, DC) improves mental and physical performance and co-ordination, reactive muscle patterns, stimulates improved movement of the spine and between bones and corrects many of the problems already mentioned. Hyperton X is also brilliant at restoring range of movement potential lost because of trauma. Here I can explain only the simplest – but nonetheless effective – form of the technique.

When visiting a therapist, muscles are usually tested whilst the athlete is standing or lying still –

and with straight legs. This almost never happens in sport, the very nature of which is movement. If the athlete's muscles test strong whilst standing still with straight legs but weak when the knees are bent slightly, they have typical hypertonic muscle indications. That is no state to be in to win a match – I can think of few matches won with still or straight legs!

The most commonly affected muscles are flexor hallucis longus, flexor digitorum longus, gastrocnemius, soleus, hamstrings, gluteus maximus, upper trapezius and diaphragm. Other muscles commonly affected are quadriceps, piriformis, psoas, abdominals, sacrospinalis and sterno-cleidomastoids. However, any muscle can be affected and by careful working out of strategy it is often possible for the athlete to learn how to use the hyperton X technique personally. I have known this technique to be dismissed as 'just another osteopathic or physiotherapy technique'. Not so. The inclusion of breathing and muscle testing augment its possibilities enormously.

How to treat a hypertonic muscle

1 Find a strong indicator muscle. Use supraspinatus, quadriceps, or any other suitable muscle.
2 Extend the problem muscle as far as you can. If it causes pain, stop at that point and retreat just far enough for the pain to disappear – usually about 1 cm.
3 Retest the indicator muscle whilst holding the problem muscle in position. If the indicator muscle now goes weak, then the problem muscle is hypertonic.
4 Keep the athlete's problem muscle in extension, blocking it from moving back with one or both hands.
5 The athlete takes a deep breath and, while *exhaling, gently* fires the muscle as though to

contract it to return it towards a normal position. This must be done slowly, over a count of 8 seconds.
6 The athlete relaxes the problem muscle and it will now extend further than before. Take up the slack. It is important to do this slowly to allow the muscle time to readjust. This is now the new starting position.
7 Repeat stages 4–6 up to three times.
8 Retest as in Stages 2 and 3. The indicator muscle should now stay strong.

It is important that the muscle is only worked on with resistance when the athlete breathes out. Many people stop breathing, or push when inhaling, which will only worsen the problem.

The great advantage of this technique is that the athlete is in control all the time, but if s/he is over-enthusiastic to get the muscles to work again, insist on the athlete using only enough pressure (10-20 per cent only) to fire the muscle against your resistance.

This technique is particularly successful where problems occur as the result of repetitive movements requiring specific muscle contraction (as in a stride length which has certain parameters). The muscles concerned have a great potential than that used in the stride length, and it is as though the particular muscle thinks that the stride length *is* its complete potential and therefore switches off at that point as it has done so often as part of the stride.

Proprioceptive integration techniques (PIT)

(Or what to do when you can't get a response from your testing.)

An indicator muscle is often required as a means of judging the integrity or state of health of some other part of the body. For this you need a muscle which will react normally and weaken or strengthen when asked. One of the pitfalls not mentioned before is that a strong muscle may be 'over strong' – so switched on that nothing will weaken it in the normal manner – and thus give false results if you use it as an indicator muscle.

Alternatively, the athlete may have a muscle so switched off that nothing you do seems to switch it on, even though there is nothing apparently wrong

with it. A normal muscle has a balance with its opposite number (or antagonist). Each allows the other facilitation and inhibition, rather like a pulley or see-saw system – when one is up the other is down and vice versa.

To test for normal muscle reactions, use the origin and insertion technique:

1 Select a muscle that tests strong.
2 Pull the two ends of the muscle apart and pinch the middle of the muscle together.
3 A normal muscle will react by becoming weak.
4 Restore it by pushing the ends of the muscle together and spreading the middle of the muscle.

5 A normal muscle will now test strong again and is a useful indicator muscle.

There are seven muscle conditions, or states of contraction/relaxation:

Testing the agonist (main muscle or prime mover)
1 Lack of facilitation (hypo-flacid) – having no contraction at all of the insertion towards the origin.
2 Over-facilitation (hypo-frozen).
3 Under-facilitation (hypo) – a muscle 'weak in the clear'.
4 Homeostatsis – a normal muscle as described above.

Testing the antagonist (or opposing muscle)
5 Under-inhibition (hyper) – a strong muscle in the clear.
6 Over-inhibition (hyper-frozen).
7 Lack of inhibition (hyper-flacid) – flacid in the extended state.

To test the agonist, or main muscle, move the two ends of the muscle close together and ask the athlete to hold whilst you pull the two ends apart. This is what you have been doing up to now and is normal muscle testing. To test the antagonist or opposing muscle, move the two ends of the muscle apart, ask the athlete to hold and then push them together.

PIT I

Hypo-frozen or over-facilitation – you are unable to weaken this muscle using origin/insertion technique.
Correct by the athlete contracting the muscle and holding it in contraction. You attempt to contract it further. This sedates the main muscle.

PIT II

Hypo-tonic muscle – the antagonist is strong and the main muscle is weak.
Correct by the athlete stretching the muscle and holding it in extension while you attempt to contract it.

PIT III

Hyper-frozen or over-inhibition – you are unable to weaken the antagonist.
Correct by the athlete putting the muscle into extension and holding it while you attempt to push it into further extension. This tones up the main muscle.

PIT IV

Hyper-tonic – the antagonist is weak and the main muscle is strong.
Correct by the athlete contracting the muscle and holding it in contraction, while you attempt to push it into extension.

Each technique should be repeated firmly several times. Retest afterwards in the same way as you did to find out which PIT technique to use. Check the muscle on the opposite side of the body, too. It will always do the opposite to the main muscle (i.e. if right pectoralis major clavicular (PMC) is hyper, left PMC will be hypo), so sometimes it is useful to work on the opposite side of the body first.

Range of motion improvement

Almost every athlete would like to improve their range of movement to give greater freedom and power as long as it does not cause instability and loss of balance. Skin pinching, tonic neck reflexes, hyperton X, reactive muscles and other more complicated techniques not mentioned here all do this. In fact, they return the body to a 'normal' that it has forgotten about.

I often position an athlete in front of a mirror that has grid lines on it, ask them to close their eyes and stand up straight. Then, when they open their eyes and look in the mirror with the grid for reference, to see the distortion in their reflection – eyes, ears, shoulders, elbow crease, hands, hip bones, knees and feet are so often slightly off centre, turned in or out, or not level.

The distortion they now see (and immediately try to correct!) surprises them because, when the eyes were closed, they felt straight. What felt right and felt straight was the result of adaptations their body has made and they have got so used to that they accept it as the norm, when in fact it is not. The grid clearly shows the distortion, and brings home the need for balanced muscle use. With distortion there is less flexibility and range of movement, speed and co-ordination. Often the difference between the ability of the right and left sides is more a matter of flexibility than strength.

Skin pinching

Just as a muscle has an antagonist to work against it, so the skin over that muscle has to stretch or contract in the same way. The skin contains pacinian corpuscles which sense skin stretch and vibration, so one way to affect the body's knowledge of its muscular state is to change the skin tension over that muscle.

For example, if the hamstrings are weak, stretch the skin over the quadriceps in the direction it would normally be stretched if the hamstrings were contracting. Stretch it as much as the skin will give without causing pain or damage. If the quads' skin stretch is involved in the hamstring's problem, the hamstring will now test strong. Unfortunately, this correction will not last more than 30 seconds, regardless of how vigorously you stretch the skin on the quadriceps.

To make it longer-lasting, you need to add another factor – vibration. Stretch the skin as before, but at the same time also vibrate your fingertips fast for about 30 seconds. This seems to 'set' the skin and muscle.

In addition, foods containing the full range of vitamin B group will help.

Aural inhibition

Occasionally, turning the head right round to the left or right will make an indicator muscle go weak. This means that any other muscle that is being used at the same time as the head is turned will go weak – not a situation one wants to happen when going for a win!

To correct, take hold of the athlete's ears, especially the curled-over edges at the top. Pull firmly away from the ear hold and uncurling the curled bits as you go. Continue round and down to the earlobe (always pulling away from the ear hole). Retest with the head turned, first to the left, then to the right, as before. This will also improve balance.

Visual inhibition

Eye direction is very important to the balance of the head on the body and as above, muscles should not go weak if the eyes are turned in any one direction.

To correct, find an indicator muscle which is strong when the athlete is looking straight forward. Retest – looking up, down, right, left and all diagonal directions – without moving the head. I even find it worth swivelling the eyes clockwise and anticlockwise and right–left–right–left. Whichever direction weakens the indicator muscle is the one that needs treatment. Visually the eye ball appears to jump rather than move smoothly at the point of direction needing treatment.

Ask the athlete to look in that direction while you (or the athlete) massage the point K-27 and the tummy button (K-27 is immediately under the collarbone, immediately next to the breastbone). Massage firmly for 30 seconds – the points may be tender.

A useful extension of this technique is to test the

specific focal length needed for the sport in question by placing an object at that distance and testing an indicator muscle or having the athlete look at the arm, hand, leg, foot position that is specifically involved in the sport and testing the muscle that is used in that position in that sport. Often the muscle will be strong until the athlete looks at it. Correct by looking in the direction or at the muscle and massaging K-27 and tummy button firmly for 30 seconds as the athlete continues to look. Retest. The indicator muscle or muscle involved in the sport should now be strong.

Atlas/occiput and tonic neck reflexes

Following the visual inhibition (above), there may be inhibition or inhibited range of motion when bending the neck.

Atlas/occiput

1 The athlete lies on his or her back and tucks the chin in. If a previously strong indicator now becomes weak, a correction is needed.
2 The athlete lies on his or her back, raises the head and tucks the chin in. If a previously strong indicator muscle now becomes weak, correction is needed here too.

To correct, place the athlete's head in the position that causes weakness. Place one hand on the forehead, one under the back of the head. The athlete now presses up against your hands which resist the movement. Repeat four or five times.

Tonic neck reflexes

This is a part of a more complicated technique, but is simple and useful, nonetheless. To improve neck flexibility and balance and co-ordination of the head with the rest of the body, proceed as follows.

1 The athlete bends the head forward.
2 Note how far it will go and then the athlete lifts the head back to the central or normal, position, then with the athlete passive, you bend the athlete's head gently forward. If it now goes further, treatment is needed.
3 Repeat with the head back, head turned to the side and head tipped to the side. In each case, where passive movement of the athlete gives greater flexibility, treat by doing the opposite, i.e. for poor head forward bends, treat with head back bends. If head turning to the right is poor, treat with head tilted to left; head tilted to left poor, treat with head turned to right.
4 In each case move the head from its central upright position only a small way in the selected direction and then press on the top of the head straight down towards the centre of the body and feet. Move it a small way further and press down again. It may take five or six small movements to accomplish one correction. Retest as for stages 1–3. You should now have improved range of movement.

Stress receptors

These are points, mostly on the skull, which seem to store stress from muscles. Each muscle identifies with a specific point on the skull (see Figure 59). Use these points if a muscle keeps going weak for no apparent reason - maybe the cranium (skull) is storing the stress.

How to test

1 Find a strong indicator muscle. Touch the stress centres. If the indicator muscle goes weak then that point needs treatment.
2 Press firmly in all the directions indicated on the diagram and find which direction causes the greatest weakness in the indicator muscle.
3 Massaging in that direction, now find which phase of breathing returns the indicator to strength. (Breathe in as you massage and test, breathe out as you massage and test.) Usually the correction is on breathing in. Repeat the direc-

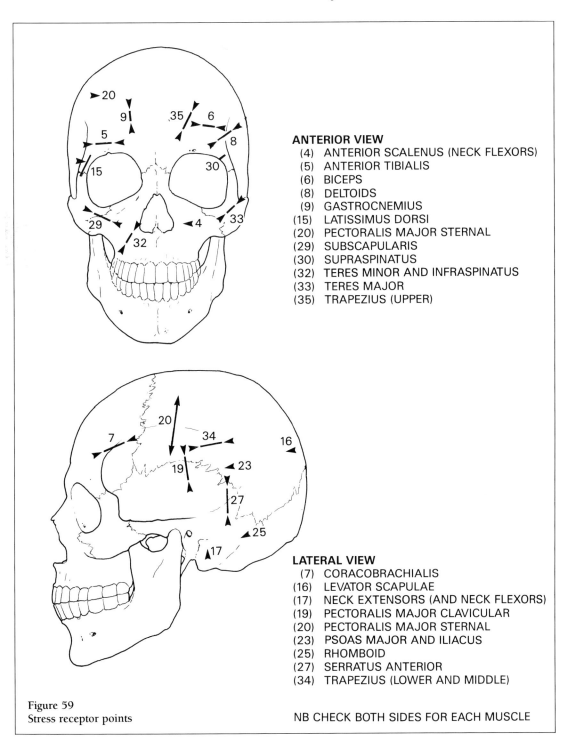

ANTERIOR VIEW
(4) ANTERIOR SCALENUS (NECK FLEXORS)
(5) ANTERIOR TIBIALIS
(6) BICEPS
(8) DELTOIDS
(9) GASTROCNEMIUS
(15) LATISSIMUS DORSI
(20) PECTORALIS MAJOR STERNAL
(29) SUBSCAPULARIS
(30) SUPRASPINATUS
(32) TERES MINOR AND INFRASPINATUS
(33) TERES MAJOR
(35) TRAPEZIUS (UPPER)

LATERAL VIEW
(7) CORACOBRACHIALIS
(16) LEVATOR SCAPULAE
(17) NECK EXTENSORS (AND NECK FLEXORS)
(19) PECTORALIS MAJOR CLAVICULAR
(20) PECTORALIS MAJOR STERNAL
(23) PSOAS MAJOR AND ILIACUS
(25) RHOMBOID
(27) SERRATUS ANTERIOR
(34) TRAPEZIUS (LOWER AND MIDDLE)

Figure 59
Stress receptor points

NB CHECK BOTH SIDES FOR EACH MUSCLE

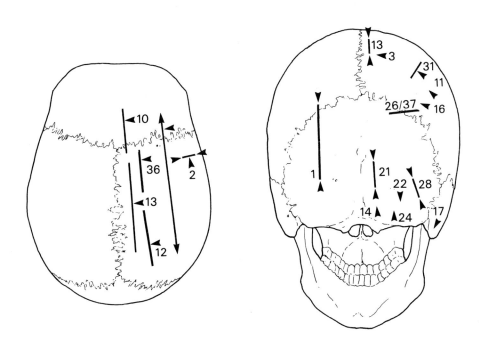

POSTERIOR AND SUPERIOR VIEW
- (1) ABDOMINIS (RECTUS)
- (2) ABDOMINIS (TRANSVERSE)
- (3) ADDUCTORS
- (10) GLUTEUS MAXIMUS
- (11) GLUTEUS MEDIUS
- (12) GLUTEUS MINIMUS
- (37) GRACILIS
- (13) HAMSTRINGS
- (14) ILEOCAECAL
- (16) LEVATOR SCAPULAE
- (17) NECK EXTENSORS AND FLEXORS
- (18) PECTORALIS MAJOR CLAVICULAR
- (21) PIRIFORMIS
- (22) POPLITEUS
- (24) QUADRATUS LUMBORUM
- (26) SARTORIUS
- (28) SOLEUS
- (31) TENSOR FASCIA LATA
- (36) TRICEPS

Figure 59
Stress receptor points   NB CHECK BOTH SIDES FOR EACH MUSCLE

tion which causes weakness and the phase of breathing that corrects it five or six times.

4 Retest as in stage 1. The stress receptor should now no longer cause the indicator muscle to weaken on touching and the muscle it belongs to will also now be strong and remain strong.

Gait and Cloacal

To accomplish even the simplest action requires co-ordination between muscles to the extent that they are fired or inhibited in the correct order to maintain balance and economy of effort and movement. When this co-ordination is upset because of injury or adaptation to a past unresolved injury, then the body fights against itself and the athlete becomes overtired very easily, especially if the muscles concerned are large postural muscles (as might be used in walking or running).

The pairs of muscles suggested below (and shown in Figure 60) should be strong when tested alone and strong when tested together to balance the body. Always correct by holding *opposite* hand and foot points for 30 seconds. (This is an exception to the general rule on holding points.) It is quite possible that whilst holding the points that you will become aware of a pulse. Wait till it is slow and even on both limbs. If you feel nothing hold and wait anyway.

Posterior gait

The athlete lies face down and raises one arm (triceps and posterior deltoid) and one leg (gluteus maximus and hamstrings). Simultaneous pressure is exerted on the arm and leg and the result is noted. To correct any weakness showing, hold SP-3 and T-3. SP-3 is on the heel side of the big toe joint on the side of the foot. T-3 is on the back of the hand half-way between the base of the ring finger and the wrist crease. Repeat test and correction if needed on opposite arm and leg. Retest.

Anterior gait

The athlete lies face up and raises an arm (anterior deltoid) and opposite leg (rectus femoris, quadriceps). Test by pressing down on both arm and leg together. Repeat with the other pair. Correct weakness by holding LV-2 and LI-3. LV-2 is on the top of the foot at the joint between the base of the big toe and second toe. LI-3 is half-way along the bone below the base of the index finger as it extends back into the webbing with the thumb. Retest.

Lateral gait

The athlete lies face up and extends opposite arm and leg out to the side (deltoid, supraspinatus and gluteus medius). Repeat to the other sides. Correct weakness by holding S-43 and H-8. S-43 is at the joint between the base of the second and third toes on the top of the foot. H-8 is on the palm of the hand on the crease below the joint between ring and little fingers. Retest.

Contra-lateral gait

The athlete sits, raises the right knee towards the left should (gluteus medius, tensor fascia lata and abdominals oblique/transverse). Put the athlete's hands across the chest to get them out of the way and push the knee and shoulder apart. Repeat the other side. Correct weakness by holding GB-41 and CX-8. GB-41 is on the top of the foot half-way between the base of the fourth and little toes and the ankle crease. CX-8 is on the palm of the hand on the crease running across the hand and below the middle finger.

Adductors/latissimus dorsi

Test these two muscles (one leg, one arm) on opposite sides of the body simultaneously by pulling one leg and one arm out sideways and repeat with the other sides. Correct any weakness by holding B-65 and L-10. B-65 is on the outside of the foot at the base of the little toe. L-10 is on the palm on the middle of the ball of the thumb.

Psoas/PMC

The athlete lies on his or her back. Test on opposite sides of the body by raising the athlete's straight leg

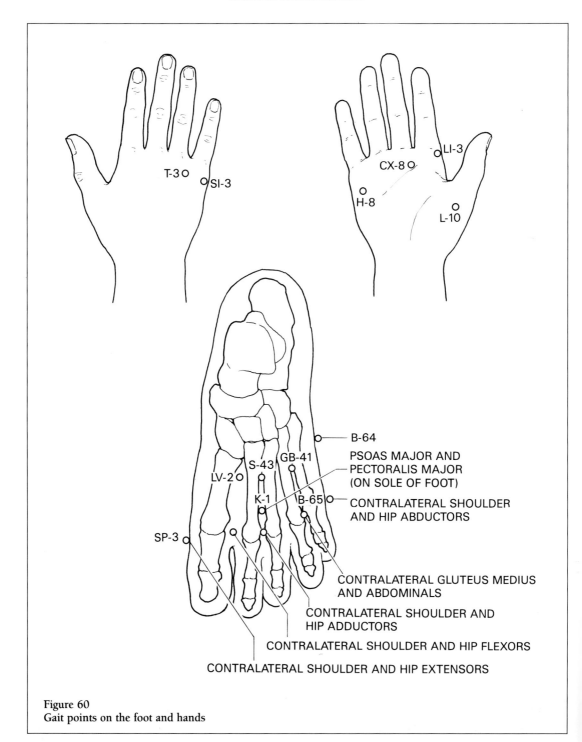

Figure 60
Gait points on the foot and hands

and arm and pushing down and out 45° to each side. Repeat the other sides. Correct any weakness by holding K-1 and SI-3. K-1 is on the under-side of the foot in the centre, just behind the ball of the foot in the crease. SI-3 is on the little-finger side of the hand, half-way between the base of the little finger and the wrist crease. Retest.

Short-cut test

While you test a strong arm indicator muscle, the athlete completely encircles the ball of the foot and toes with the other hand. If the indicator muscle goes weak then there is a gait problem. Test the other foot, too. The athlete then touches all the points on the foot that caused the indicator muscle to go weak - on the big toe joint, the bases between all the toes on the top of the foot and the outside of the little toe and the K-1 point under the foot (see diagram) in turn, while you retest the indicator muscle. Any point that produces weakness in the indicator muscle needs holding with the relevant hand points on the *opposite* hand. Retest.

A less comfortable, but equally effective correction is to massage firmly on the tops of the bases of the toes (between the tendons on top of the foot) for about 30 seconds.

Cloacal

This is a technique to help synchronize cranium and sacral movements (head and pelvis). It can also help with spinal, muscular and nervous diseases which cause poor co-ordination. There are eight different combinations, four front and four back.

1. The athlete lies on his or her back and lifts the right arm (anterior deltoid) and right leg (rectus femoris), i.e. on the same side of the body. Test that each is strong on its own. Pressure is then put on both together to pull them inwards towards the waist (back ipsilateral).
2. As above, but pressure is put on them to push outwards and down to the table (front ipsilateral).
3. As in stage 1 above, but test opposite - right arm and left leg.
4. As in stage 2 above, but test opposite - right arm and left leg.
5. As in stages 1-4 above, but now using left arm and left leg or left arm and right leg.

If, when you tested, you pulled outward and found weakness, correct by anterior points - these usually accompany acute problems. If, when you tested you pushed downward and found weakness, correct with posterior points - these are for more chronic problems.

HELP

Hold the points together as they correspond to arm and leg. Wait for 30 seconds, or until a slow, balanced pulse is felt in both points.

Anterior points

Hold together the supra-orbital foramen (on the eye socket just at the inner end of the eyebrow by the top of the nose) and the top of the pubic bone half an inch to the side of centre.

Posterior points

Hold on the side of the head (temporal bone) just above and behind the top edge of the ear in a shallow depression, together with the sacrotuberous ligament (where the sacrum and coccyx meet just above the very end of the tail bone, at the point where it curls under).

Extra gaits

Extra gait 1

This is a further co-ordination technique, using two muscle tests together. The athlete lies on his or her back and raises one leg straight. (Both rectus femoris and gluteus maximus muscles must be strong.) Test by pushing down on the lifted ankle at the same time as picking the other ankle up to pull them together, like scissors.

Similarly, test with the other leg up and the first one

163

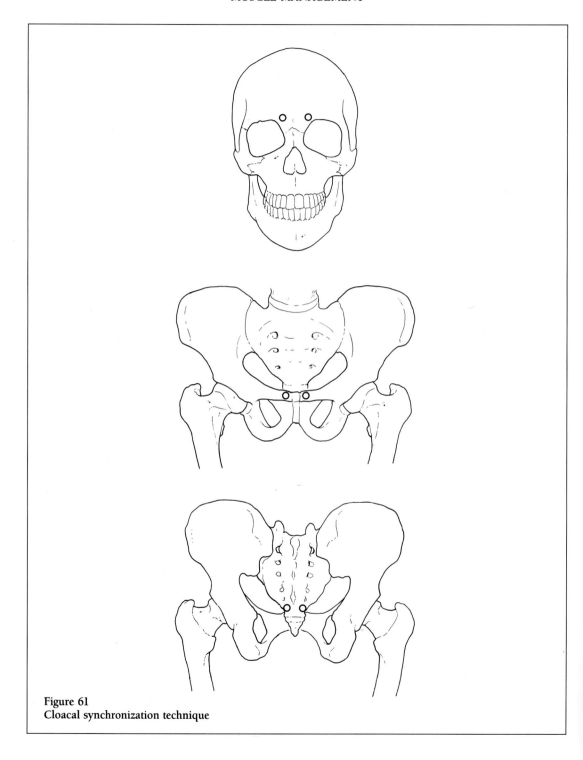

Figure 61
Cloacal synchronization technique

on the table. If either combination is weak, correct by turning the athlete over and working on the sacrum (the bone in the middle of the buttocks at the top back of the hips). Push one side up and the other down and test a hamstring or other convenient indicator muscle. Now change and test the sacrum by pushing the other way round. Find the direction of pushing on the sacrum that causes the hamstrings to weaken and push in that direction as the athlete breathes in. Repeat this four or five times.

You do not have to push hard, but it must be synchronized with breathing in. Turn the athlete back over and test the straight leg as before. Both combinations should now be strong.

Extra gait 2

Now take both legs out to one side whilst the athlete grips the table with the hands. Ask the athlete to hold the legs out as you push in. Repeat the other side. Again, each gluteus medius, quadratus lumborum and adductors should be strong before you start. If the extra gait problem exists here, pulling both legs together in to the centre without supporting the hips will cause weakness to one side.

Correct by pushing up on the lower outside of the hip joint one side and down on the top outer edge of the hip-bone the other side. Test a good indicator muscle such as anterior deltoid; then test the oppo-site hip combination. Push on the combination that gives a weak indicator muscle, together with breathing in four or five times. Retest, taking the legs out to the previously weak side. The legs should now test strong.

Extra gait 3

The same technique can be used with the arms.

(a) *For arm flexors and extensors* – use the leg scissor effect you used before on the arms. Correct weakness by testing the two collar bones either side of the breastbone, pushing one up and one down and testing an indicator muscle. Then choose the direction that causes indicator weakness and repeat it four or five times whilst breathing in. Retest the arm scissors.

(b) *For arm abductors and adductors* – take both arms to one side, push back in and then test the other side. If either combination goes weak, then the shoulder girdle needs correction. Push one shoulder up and one down; test an indicator muscle, then repeat the other way round. Choose the direction that caused indicator muscle weakness and repeat four or five times while breathing in. Retest the arms to the previously weak side. The arms should not be strong.

Right/left brain dominance and cross crawl

Few people are ambidextrous and therefore most of us have one side of the brain dominant. It has been noted, however, that we function best in any activity involving neurological and brain integration or cross-motor patterned activity. This means both sides of the brain working together.

Each side of the brain has its own function: one side – usually the left – is analytical and logical, linear, time orientated, judgemental. The other side (usually the right) deals with spacial awareness, perception of the whole, rhythm, music and imagination. Most activities require both types of thinking.

To test for brain integration, have the athlete look at a large X shape –X. Test an indicator muscle (e.g. anterior deltoid or supraspinatus or PMC). Then have the athlete look at a shape showing two parallel lines -// and test an indicator muscle. The in-dicator muscle should be strong on X and weak on //. If not, whatever the combination is, there may be hesitation in physical activity and correction is needed.

The athlete should exercise by marching on the spot, lifting the knees high and touching one knee with the opposite elbow at the same time. Right knee and left elbow, left knee and right elbow. Repeat 25 times. The reason for touching elbow to knee is to ensure co-ordination which is often lacking in those whose muscles do not test strong to X and weak to //. This is cross-crawl and uses the right and left sides of the brain together.

Intersperse repetitions or cross-crawl with homo-lateral march - raising the right arm and right leg together, followed by left arm and left leg. Keep swopping over until cross-crawl is easy and the athlete tests strong on X and weak on //. It may take a week or two, but will vastly improve co-ordination and will help those people who always come back exhausted after a training run.

Co-ordination can be improved even further by doing the psoas bounce (see psoas muscle, page 93).

Carpal tunnel and pisiform/hamate syndromes

These are hand problems which can be the source of tingling, weak or numb hands, painful hands, wrists, elbows and shoulders. The cause is entrapment of the nerves. These pass down to the fingers from the neck and have to run the gauntlet of narrow spaces at the neck, shoulder, elbow and – worst of all – the wrist joint.

The arm nerves divide into two parts: one (median) – affecting the thumb, index and middle finger, which can become trapped in the carpal tunnel in the wrist; the other (ulnar), which affects the ring and little finger, can become trapped at the base of the little finger between two bones, the pisiform and the hamate.

Typically, both of these conditions can result from collisions with other players, or the wall of a squash court or problems with gripping the racket or club, or where there is constant stretching, twisting and flicking of the palm (or wrist), or small precise finger movements as in cricket, bowling, shot-putt, darts,

etc. They can also result from over-use of a specific hand muscle which causes the tendon sheath to swell and squash the nerve as it passes through the wrist space (normally a tight fit at the best of times).

How to test

1 First test by using the general test for hand muscles (see page 65) and attempt to strengthen in the usual way with the help points. If this is unsuccessful, proceed as given in stages 2-4.
2 Ask the athlete to encircle the wrist with the thumb and index finger of the other hand, holding very gently as if the wrist were something precious and breakable and retest using the general test.
3 Test with palm facing up and palm facing down.
4 Watch to see if the thumb or little finger now weakens most. If it is the thumb, correct it with carpal tunnel technique. If it is the little finger, use pisiform/hamate technique.

Carpal tunnel

This is malfunction of the thumb and index fingers due to the nerve being squashed as it goes through the very narrow space between the many small wrist bones. These are held together by a strong band of ligament and the pronator quadratus muscle. Correction is effected by adjusting the two forearm bones. Hold the athlete's hand with the fingers of your two hands and place your thumbs above the wrist joint along the forearm. Establish the direction of adjustment by light brushing thumbs together or thumbs apart across the wrist bone with your two thumbs. Retest after each direction. If brushing the thumbs together strengthens the general hand muscle test, then the correction needed is to squeeze the two splayed forearm bones together. However I have found far more frequently that brushing the thumbs

apart will strengthen the general hand muscle test and this means that the two forearm bones are jammed together and should be gently separated by thumb pressure against the forearm bones out sideways, all the way from the wrist to the elbow.

Points to hold

Acupoints LI-4 and H-3. LI-4 is on the 'back' of the hand at the end of the crease when the thumb and index finger are held together. H-3 is at the inner end of the crease on the inside of the elbow. (See Figure 62.)

If the wrist is sensitive, support it for two weeks with strapping or Tubi grip. Eating foods rich in B vitamins will help.

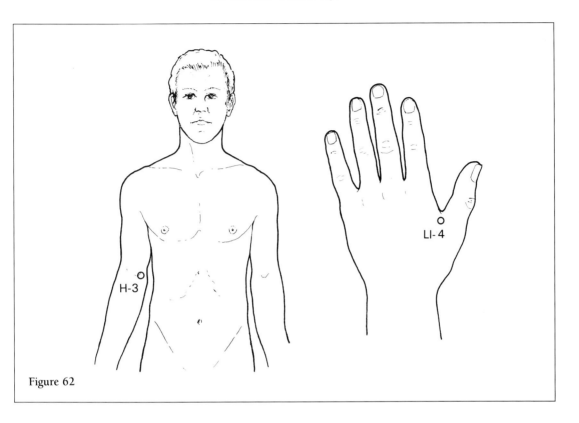

Figure 62

Pisiform/hamate

This malfunction of the little finger and ring finger is caused by the nerve being squashed because the bones at the base of the little finger near the wrist are out of place. Test for correction direction as follows.

1 The athlete holds up the palm of the hand and you test by pressing first on the palm at the base of the little finger just above the wrist crease where the pisiform is, a nobbly pea sized bone, and by retesting the general hand muscle test.
2 Then the athlete holds the hand palm down. Press on the back of the hand just above the wrist and the base of the little finger (just opposite the little nobbly bone on the palm), and retest the general hand muscle test. Whichever makes the muscle test strong is the direction needed for correction.
3 Take hold of the two sides of the athlete's hand

(palm up or palm down as already decided) with the fingers of your two hands and put both thumbs on the bone you are correcting (at the base of the little finger side of the hand). The athlete's arm should be totally relaxed, as you pull very gently and press sharply on the bone with your thumbs - it's as though you flick the arm somewhat like a whip from the contact point of your thumbs. Speed is more important than pressure.
4 Retest with the general hand muscle test.

The athlete can help the correction hold by eating extra foods that contain B vitamins.

It is also advisable in both carpal tunnel and pisiform/hamate to check that the general hand muscles are not reactive to pronator teres, brachioradialis or any other arm muscle.

Shock absorbers

The joints of the body have two actions. The first is obvious – to allow movement and provide a fulcrum for lifting. The second reason is to provide shock-absorbing properties to prevent the shock of the body weight as it hits the ground (or other hard object) from travelling back up the limbs to the spine. Almost all sports require this effect to shield us from jumping, racquet or bat hitting balls, etc.

How to test the leg shock absorbers

1 The athlete lies on his or her back and a strong straight leg indicator muscle is found (quads, gluteus medius, etc.).
2 Hit the bottom of the heel sharply (after having warned the athlete!) and retest. If it remains strong there are no leg shock-absorber problems.
3 If it weakens, bend the knee and direct a blow on the knee towards the hip and retest. If the straight leg indicator is now strong the problem is in the ankle.
4 If the indicator muscle is weak, pick up the athlete's thigh with both hands and drive it sharply into the hip joint. If the straight leg indicator muscle is now strong the problem is in the knee.
5 If the straight leg indicator is weak the problem is in the hip.

To correct the ankle
Having waggled the ankle gently to relax the foot, turn the foot inwards as though doing a posterior tibial test. Then with both hands pull once, sharply, but lightly away from the head. This should release the ankle. Retest as in stage 2 above.

To correct the knee
Bend the athlete's knee, sliding your forearm under the knee between calf and thigh, and with the other hand holding the foot, sharply and lightly bend the knee further. Alternatively, sit on the athlete's foot of the bent leg and pull the top of the calf sharply towards you once to free the knee joint. Retest as in stage 3 above.

To correct the hip
Take the athlete's straight leg out to the side at about 30°. Hold the athlete's ankle between your thighs, grasp the athlete's leg above the knee with both hands and pull once past and sharply away from the hip joint to release it.

How to test the arm shock absorbers

The same ways of testing and correction apply to the arm, expect that it is recommended to test by hitting the clenched fist of the athlete's arm that has been taken 90° away from the body. You need less force to correct the arm problems, as these joints generally are not weight bearing and are more mobile than leg joints.

Scar tissue

Sometimes old injury or operation scars itch and pull. Perhaps they are no trouble at all until there is another injury at, or near, that site and then there is poor healing of the new injury or continued pain. The scar does not have to be large, and often it is the stitch-hole scars rather than the major scars that are the nuisance.

large scar may need touching along its length – and retest. Wherever the indicator muscle goes weak, treatment is needed, but do *not* work on a scar that has not properly healed yet. Scars that are more than six weeks old are usually OK. Six-month-old scars should cause no problems, yet it is often just about that time that the itching and pulling starts.

How to test

Find a strong indicator muscle. Touch the scar - a

HELP

Using pain-relieving spray (containing fluromethane

and available at any chemist), freeze the part of the scar that needs treatment till the surface is white (but not frost-bitten!) and stretch across the scar as though trying to pull it apart. (With round scars, stretch in all directions away from the centre.) Warm

it up again with your hands and retest. The indicator muscle should now stay strong. Neither freezing alone nor stretching alone will do it. It has to be both together to de-activate the weakening effect. It may occasionally be necessary to repeat the treatment.

Shoe lifts

Your feet are your foundation and as I have said earlier in this book, bad shoes are a menace. It is better to work without them than wear 'old horrors' that only compound postural problems because of the way you have worn them down. If you doubt me, take a pencil, place it anywhere under the foot and toes and test any good indicator muscle and see what you get!

If, for some anatomical reason, the athlete needs to use a shoe lift inside the shoe (after a broken leg, for instance) go to a good podiatrist. However, there is something you can do to help the athlete in the meantime to find the right height of temporary shoe lift and where to put it.

How to test

1 Whilst the athlete is sitting, find a good indicator muscle.
2 Retest as the athlete stands, barefoot.
3 Retest with the athlete wearing training shoes.
4 If either of these test weak, find an old telephone book, or a magazine or two, and estimate how many pages the athlete will need to stand on (and with which foot) to bring the hips level, as follows.
5 By trial and error, muscle testing as you go till you

get a good strong indicator muscle, find out exactly how many pages are needed. Draw an outline round the foot, cut the pages out and bind with sellotape.
6 Now move it around under the foot to see where the lift is needed (front/back, inside/outside, or under the whole foot). Again, look for the strongest indicator muscle strength.
7 Shape the temporary shoe lift you have made accordingly and fit it into the athlete's shoe.
8 A good fit will give a strong indicator muscle when the athlete is wearing both shoes.
9 Where healing time is needed after a fracture you may need to alter it at weekly intervals for a while, removing a few 'pages' as the leg and pelvic muscles regain tone and alter the foot balance.

The above method gives you a very accurate (if amateurish) way of handling a problem and preventing further misalignment of the hips etc., providing you monitor it properly until you can get professionally fitted orthotics.

You should have room to wriggle your toes inside your training shoes. A too snug fit that squashes the toes back against the foot will switch off neck muscles and cause neck problems.

Ileocaecal valve syndrome

Indigestion and bowel problems are very prevalent amongst athletes because of the stresses, strains and poor eating habits they inflict upon themselves in order to succeed. The most frequent cause is a malfunction of the ileocaecal valve (ICV).

This valve is a supposedly one-way valve between the large and small intestine, letting the digesting food pass through from the small intestine (where most of the vitamins, minerals and other goodies are

drawn out into the bloodstream) to the large intestine (where it is already beginning to putrify and become toxic and bacteria-laden due to the length of time it has been in the body). So, a constant procession of the bowel contents is a good idea.

Malfunction causes congestion and either a build-up or a back-flow (depending on whether the valve is in spasm or flaccid), followed by a bizarre list of symptoms including bloating and distension, flatu-

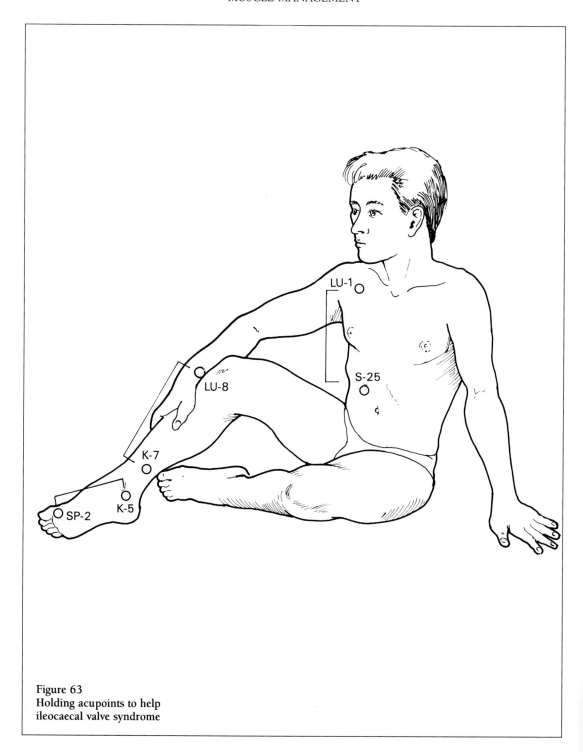

Figure 63
Holding acupoints to help
ileocaecal valve syndrome

lence, wandering pain, constipation, headaches, migraines or nausea, neck and shoulder pain, low back pain, diarrhoea, difficulty getting going in the morning and general malaise, sudden thirst, paleness and black rings round the eyes.

To test and correct

Draw an imaginary line from the athlete's navel to the top outside of the right hip. Find the middle of this line and go down about an inch towards the knees.

You are now over the ileocaecal valve. Press in gently and test a previously strong indicator muscle. If it goes weak, the athlete has the problem. Replace your hand on the abdomen by the athlete's hand. Retest. If the indicator is still weak, then the problem is priority (i.e. fix it before you do anything else). Place your own hand on top of the athlete's hand, and use the SNEAK test (see pages 147-148) to see what type of correction is needed. The combination of SNEAK and the athlete's hand on the ICV that produces a strong indicator is the type of correction needed.

If structure is indicated, do not do structural or soft tissue or visceral work unless you are a trained chiropractor of osteopath. The ICV is almost directly above the appendix which inexperienced hands could rupture. Do the acupoints and food and ESR corrections for now and send the athlete to see an Applied Kinesiologist.

If nutrition shows up as being needed, the athlete should avoid all stimulants such as tea, coffee, alcohol and all raw high-fibre foods and should cook all vegetables because the ICV is already overstimulated. They must eat foods high in B vitamins and calcium. After two weeks they can gradually introduce high-fibre foods again, starting with bananas and grated apple and progressing to a normal diet with lots of raw foods. Eat only when relaxed and - this is most important - chew everything well and continue to avoid any food that causes flatulence or which you suspect might be an allergen.

If you are competing in a highly stressed sports meeting, it is far better to eat well the day before (see Pritikin, details in Bibliography) and rest your digestive system on the day.

If emotion shows up, turn to Chapter 6 and work with whatever is appropriate.

If acupuncture shows up, work with the acupoints (see Figure 63).

CHAPTER 7

Stress, the will to win and time out of mind

Stress is not what happens but how you react to it. 'A good athlete does not experience failure - just mistakes.' (L.E. Unestahl)

These two sentences epitomize the mental aspects of sport, the mental side of the triad of health described in Chapter 1. This chapter is devoted to what can go wrong in sport, what to do about it and when. Just as some terminal cancer patients can reverse their disease by thought, so athletes can promote or sabotage their efforts. The power of the mind is enormous.

Many, many accidents and injuries happen in sport when there is a mismatch of task difficulty and arousal state, causing changes in the balance between the athlete's actual and their perceived skill - either the athlete becomes careless or is pushing himself or herself too hard and is over-anxious. Both are mental malpractice - what you think about matters most.

The techniques presented here are mostly used before or after the physical activity and so are preventive analysis and positive building of self-esteem. They are to be used when the athlete is waiting to get on court, during a lunch-break, on a train journey, when it is too wet or too cold to play, when there is injury - or anything else that prevents getting at the physical side of things.

Good mental practice involves clear, clean thinking. You need to seek out the mental glitches in the system that lessen physical performance and align all your thoughts towards success.

But before you can begin the game of debugging and strategic planning you need to know what the situation is now. It may be obvious - the athlete is waiting for an injury to heal, or vague - the athlete can't seem to avoid this or that cropping up again and again and you don't know why.

WOTS SO (Wins, 'Orrors, Technicalities, Situations, Sort Out)

It is necessary, first, to take out paper and pencil and write down the facts about the 'now' situation. (An old saying goes, 'You can't get from London to Birmingham till you know where London is.')

Now rewrite the list in as non-judgemental and impersonal a way as you can. Sometimes it helps to do this together with another trainer or athlete in a

trusting frame of mind, particularly with one who is interested but uninvolved in the problem. Here are some examples from the two lists, the first list finding all the negative stories you or the athlete sell yourselves to excuse failure.

I ought to do well because . . . but . . .

I can do it in practice, but . . .

It's OK to play for me, but not OK to play for . . .

I'm fine till just before . . .

They think I ought to . . . but . . .

Fill in the sentences – I'm sure you can think of plenty more of your own.

The WOTS SO list changes attitudes, not facts. It removes the judgement, so that, 'I ought to do well because . . .' becomes, 'I have the ability to . . .' 'I want to do well because . . .' becomes, 'I especially enjoy the feeling when . . .'

A typical non-judgemental analysis of a weekend golfer, within the context of ability and time available, might be:

Handicap of 18, playing twice a month and almost no practice.

Woods – Good length, sometimes finishing to the left.

Long irons – Good. Occasionally pulls.

Medium irons – Good strike. Occasionally shanks.

Short iron – Good strike. Inconsistent aim.

Putting – Variable.

Such a series of statements tells the truth rather than a collection of hopes, fears and sorrows, and you can then decide what is next, i.e., what you want to do about each part or if there is one overall fault. It will also cheer up the pessimist and take the over-confident, uncritical athlete down a peg and get them interested in real progress in the sport rather than ego polishing.

First, I will discuss debugging, clearing out the rubbish and spring cleaning for the strategic planning which comes later.

Problems can be anything from 'the magnetic gorse bush on the eighth hole I always seem to hit my golf ball into', to the seventeen-mile barrier in a marathon where all the energy is gone and the negative thoughts pile up and only will-power gets the athlete through to the finish.

Problems can be divided into two main categories: inner and outer; and within these, acute, chronic and phobic. How the athlete plays now depends not only on a perfect match of skill to situation, but also on everything past and present, good and bad, that has happened. 'Now results from then, so then affects now.' Figure 64 shows how stress and other factors can affect performance.

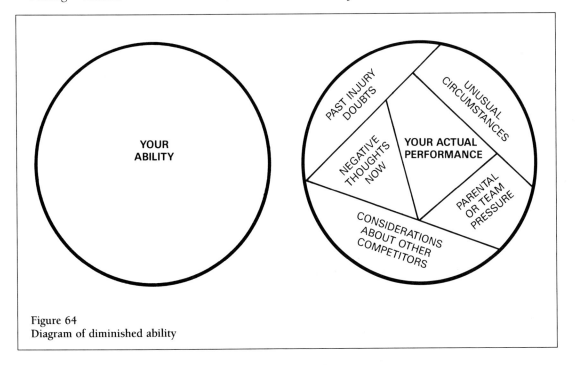

Figure 64
Diagram of diminished ability

But remember than anything bad is an opportunity for improvement. Inner stress is all the things you think about that lessen your own self-esteem, and outer stress is all the things 'they' do to you – be they parents, track officials, other athletes or whatever.

Debugging and spring-cleaning techniques

1 Psychological reversal
2 Phobia technique
3 Emotional stress relief – past memory
4 Emotional stress relief – tissue memory
5 Emotional stress relief – present affirmations and temporal tap

6 Behavioural barometer
7 Bach Flower Remedies

These techniques allow the athlete to drop the old stories, accept WOTS SO without blame and move on to:

8 Planning
9 Visualization
10 Goal setting, goal balancing and emotional stress relief for future success.

This mental muscles management will give the athlete purpose, free them for concentration and more time and space to experience the joy of their sport.

Figure 65 charts the many techniques that can be used to help turn athlete failure into a winning situation of optimum performance.

Pyschological reversal

Failure to regain health and failure to succeed is sometimes due to self-sabotage. Although at a conscious level the athlete wants to get better, subconsciously s/he does not. Worse, some scars and injuries are worn like a trophy, an investment to explain failure or, following masochistic over-training, used in an 'I told you so' frame of mind to give time to cope with stress.

The pattern shows up when a strong indicator muscle becomes weak when the athlete states or imagines a positive goal they say they desire to achieve. When a failure or negative aspect of the goal is imagined, then the indicator muscle tests strong. (If both positive and negative aspects test weak then either it is the wrong goal or there is too much stress around the subject in general that needs clearing first.)

There are individuals who respond poorly to treatment and training and, where there is improvement, tend to dismiss it or pass over it quickly and get back to dwelling on the negative aspects.

Psychological reversal can be very specific – the athlete will test normally to the idea of sport, but reverse and test weak when a specific aspect of their own sport is mentioned. A typical example would be 'golf in general' is OK, but '18″ putts' causes a reversal. It can be a physical, mental or personal upset

and is usually related to something that that movement, idea or person represents, and often involves self-judgement in the light of it.

HELP

Immediate help can be gained by the athlete saying: 'I profoundly and deeply accept myself with all my problems and shortcomings.' This will return the muscle testing to normal, but shows up a lack of self-acceptance.

Points to tap

Acupoints SI-1 or SI-3. SI-1 is on the outside nail bed of the little finger. SI-3 is outside the little finger edge of the palm in the crease that appears when you make a fist (see Figure 66). Tap these points three times a second, while the athlete says the positive aspects of the goal out loud ten times at least. As with all stress-related subjects, eating foods with lots of Vitamin B will help, also take Rescue Remedy from the Bach Flower Remedy range for two weeks. (This is the most widely available general remedy but, if you can, turn to the notes on Bach Flower Remedies and test to find the 'Specific'.)

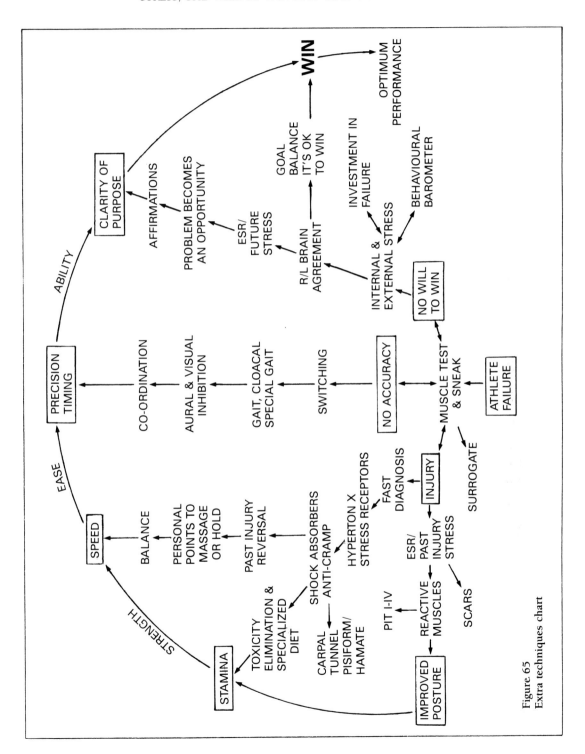

Figure 65
Extra techniques chart

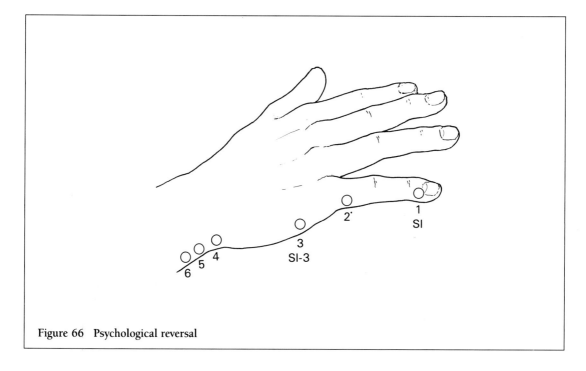

Figure 66 Psychological reversal

Bach Flower Remedies

These are a set of remedies for emotional upsets, discovered and researched by Dr Bach. There are several good publications and charts detailing the characteristics of each one.

If, when you are working with the SNEAK test (see page 147) and thumb to ring finger shows weakness on the indicator muscle or, conversely, when held together with a previously weak muscle, the muscle now becomes strong, it shows that emotion is the cause of the problem. Now all you have to do is to find out which of the 39 remedies is needed. They come in four boxes.

How to test

1 Test the muscle that is weak and put one box of the remedies on the athlete's solar plexus. Retest. If it stays weak, nothing in that box will help. Try another box, until you find which of the four boxes - there may be more than one - causes the muscle to return to strength.

2 Now open that box and put the athlete's hand over five bottles. Retest. If there's no strengthening, try the other five, one by one, till you find out which bottle is the strengthening bottle.

3 If there are more than five, maybe some are duplicating each other. Find the strongest combination.

4 Now, as a definitive test, remove all the bottles. The muscle will now be as weak as it was when the athlete started. Open the strengthening bottle and have the athlete take a good sniff and retest. If this is the right bottle, the muscle will strengthen. Read out the qualities and emotions pertaining to the bottle and you will find the athlete agrees it is right.

5 Put four drops in a small dropper bottle (10-15 ml) with spring water and take a squirt (or ten drops) every 2-4 hours. As these drops are already in homoeopathic dilution, you can't overdose and the drops become ineffective when the upset is no longer present. You can put up to

six remedies in one bottle. You may need to take it for hours only, or up to a month or more. Check by retesting.

This method takes the guesswork away from choosing the right Bach Flower Remedy. You ask the body itself by muscle testing.

Phobias

A phobia is an irrational fear which can be directed to almost any aspect of normal life. The athlete's reaction is unrealistic and out of all proportion; their body energies go haywire and their total attention is taken away from the sport and given entirely to avoidance of the phobic subject – be it flying, lifts, trains, playing in a place where something awful happened, crowds, specific colours, and so on. Often phobias severely limit an athlete's life, not just in sporting matters.

HELP

1 First you will need to clear the athlete of psychological reversal. (See page 174.) Failure to do so may mean failure to clear the phobia. Test with

the general statement, 'I want to have a good life,' and 'I want to be miserable.' Test further with the specific phobia: 'I want to get rid of my fear of (dogs),' and, 'I want to keep my fear of (dogs),' and treat as for psychological reversal if necessary.

2 Evaluate the fear of (dogs) on a 1-10 scale:

1 = I am perfectly calm and relaxed with (dogs).
10 = I can't bear it, I go straight into panic with all the discomforting degrees in-between.

Take into account that it may be OK to talk about (dogs) but if one is brought into the room, confrontation or actual proximity will cause panic and instant escape by the athlete.

3 While the athlete thinks about or confronts the

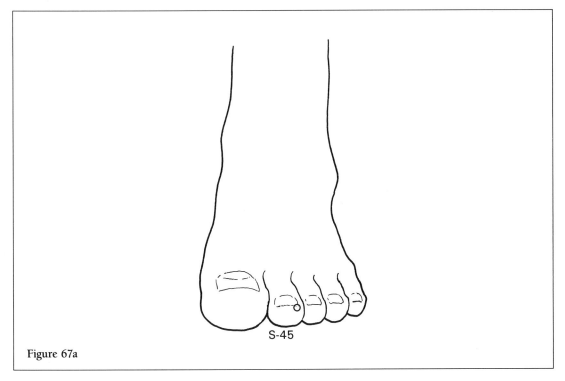

S-45

Figure 67a

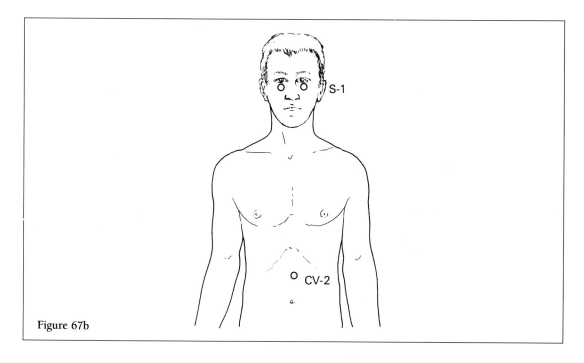

Figure 67b

phobia (i.e. the dog), test an indicator muscle and it will go weak. Then have the athlete touch a point CV-12 (which is half-way between the tummy button and the end of the breastbone) while thinking about it or confronting it again. If the indicator muscle now goes strong, tap ST-1 and S-45 thirty times while the athlete keeps on thinking about or confronting the problem. ST-1 is under the middle of each eye on the cheek bone. S-45 is on the outer edge of the nail of the second toe. (See Figure 67a.)

4 If testing as in stage 3 above is ineffective, repeat but this time the athlete touches the ends of the twelfth ribs (the lowest floating ribs at the back). If this strengthens the indicator muscles, tap K-1 and K-27 while thinking and confronting as above. K-1 is on the sole of the foot at the heel end of the crease in the centre of the ball of the foot. K-27 is in the dip below the collar-bone where it joins the breastbone. (See Figure 67b.)

5 Now confront the phobia (i.e. the dog) again immediately and reassess. For example, a claustrophobic might go into a cupboard and shut the door and then reassess the fear level. If the rating is above 2, repeat the process. On retesting, the athlete should now test strong. Where you cannot re-create the phobia (for example, as in flying), teach the athlete the points to work on unobtrusively when the situation does arise.

6 The athlete must now think about the phobia and either: (a) hum 'Happy Birthday' or 'God Save the Queen' (or anything else), then retest the indicator muscle; and/or (b) count out loud, then retest. If either of these causes a weak indicator muscle the athlete should continue thinking and confronting and now touch CV-12 or the end of the twelfth rib again whilst counting or humming (whichever one caused weakness), while you tap the points again. This will help integrate the right and left sides of the brain.

7 Retest with the athlete thinking and confronting, but with: (a) eyes open; (b) eyes closed. If eyes open causes weakness, tap the back of the head just above the neck, as s/he thinks and confronts. If eyes closed caused a weak indicator, tap the centre of the forehead while s/he thinks and confronts. Retest, eyes open and eyes closed. Both should now be strong. (This will have harmonized front and back brain.)

Emotional stress relief (ESR) and the behavioural barometer

Emotional stress relief (ESR) is an extraordinary, powerful but very simple technique. It consciously uses what for many is an instinctive, instantaneous reaction.

The help points are on either side of the forehead, half-way between the centre of each eyebrow and the hairline. Hold these points very lightly – just enough to stretch the skin. If you find the right direction you may well feel a pulse. This will be irregular and/or unbalanced between your hands (and often accompanied by rapid fluttering of the eyelids) while the athlete thinks of the stress. The irregularity this will calm, slow and balance when the stress reaction has subsided. The brain activity has changed from back brain emotion to front brain objectivity.

Stress takes many forms and ESR is useful for all of them: past, present, future, accidents and upsets, physical, mental, other people, etc. for instance, it is common to have an injury or accident after a shock such as a death in the family. The list is long, but there's basically one technique, and it is important to remember that stress is not what happens, it is how you react to it.

How to test

1 Find an indicator muscle – PMC is good.
2 The athlete thinks about the stress. Retest the indicator muscle, which will now be weak.
3 Over a period of a few minutes the athlete thinks of the stress while you hold the points on the forehead.
4 When the points have calmed down, retest the indicator muscle which will now be strong.

You need have no fear of harming the athlete. They will not respond if the subject matter is too dangerous, in which case send them for professional psychiatric advice. The worst that will happen is tears, or moving parts of the body about. If you suspect this might happen, lay the athlete on the floor and have a box of tissues handy.

'What stops you is what runs you'. Take over now. ESR doesn't change the facts, it changes your over-

reaction to them and you become objective. The beauty of the technique is its absolute privacy – the athlete only has to think of the problem, and doesn't have to tell you if s/he doesn't want to. He or she can also hold the points and think alone. However, the technique is more effective if the problem is talked about out loud as it keeps the athlete's mind on the subject. When we don't want to think about certain problems, the mind wanders! It may be necessary for the athlete to talk through the incident three or more times. You will notice that as they do so the language becomes less hysterical, highly coloured or emotional and calms down to a matter-of-fact list of events. ESR will de-stress any incident in the past that is still running the athlete's life now.

I have found the following techniques useful for assisting the process:

1 Ask the athlete to relate the incident, and ask for all the details you can think of – place, time of day, weather, who was there, what they wore, who said what, etc., – all in as much 'glorious technicolour' as possible.

Then ask the athlete to imagine making a film or video of it and to watch this and relate it as though from the outside. Wind the video back and replay twice as fast as normal, like a cartoon. Then, still in imagination, take a big pair of scissors and snip it up. Throw the bits in the air and stick it together in any order, so you have a nose stuck on a hurdle with an arm floating in the air, etc. – Nonsense! This usually makes the athlete laugh. Wind the video back again and put it in a box and throw it away. By now the athlete will normally test strong while thinking about the original incident.

2 It may be necessary to deal with different aspects of the incident if it is a very serious one. In this case, I work out the different aspects, put them all into imaginary balloons, give the athlete the balloon strings to hold and work on the biggest balloon first.

3 It may be useful when the incident is connected with a specific person, such as an over-pushing

parent, to talk in general about feelings about men or women. When there is a specific emotion such as antagonism, anger, resentment, hostility, fear, loss, grief, guilt, indifference or separation, it may help to concentrate on that word and work on different aspects of it using prompt sentences (whilst holding the ESR points) such as:

'When did you last feel (angry)?'
'How does it feel to be (angry)?'
'Who around you is (angry)?'
'Who else is (angry)?'
'What's it like to receive (anger)?'
'Where in your body do you feel (anger)?'
'What makes you (angry)?'
'What else makes you (angry)?'
'Think of something or someone else that makes you (angry).'
'Think of an incident long ago when you felt (angry).'
'When was the first time you remember feeling (angry)?'
'What would you like to have done or undone then that you didn't?'
'What would have made it all right then?'
'Think about the incident this time when you felt (angry).'

Then retest PMC, which should now be strong. Very often the athlete will see a pattern emerging through the pictures from the past, thrown up by the questions. If so, then they will be much more in control next time someone presses the emotional tender spot that caused the specific emotion.

4 It may be necessary to work through different aspects of the chosen word (e.g. 'anger') by testing the indicator against other angry words, such as seething, fuming, incensed, irritated, belligerent, furious, raging, savage, explosive, outraged, hysterical, etc., and de-stress the ones that cause the greatest weakening of the indicator muscle.

5 Then test the opposite emotion and make sure that it too doesn't weaken the indicator muscle; for example, the opposite of anger might be willing, receptive, encouraging, adequate, answerable, aware, etc.

These techniques allow the athlete choice, either to accept what is, as it is and create anew, or resist what is and control it. The best of these is the former as it allows the athlete to be 'at cause' rather than 'at effect' of the outcome of the stressful circumstances'.

If there is resistance to using these techniques, have the athlete consider the following:

1 What does it cost me?
2 What does it buy me?
3 What are the possibilities I'm missing?

Sometimes the athlete may feel it preferable to keep present friends rather than lose them by winning and moving up to a different class as a way of saying no to pushing, ambitious parents; or conversely s/he may nurse an injury that is long healed as an excuse for not admitting s/he can't bear success and besides it gets lots of attention and sympathy from friends rather than jealousy. These short-term 'buys' will cost him or her for the rest of their life unless they are defused now. Such sabotaging techniques wreck self-esteem. The athlete will end up hating the particular sport and hating him- or herself, and become an embittered person.

ESR and tissue memory

Just as the athlete will have a mental memory of a past incident, so there will be a tissue memory. Usually it is the position of landing after a fall – where the bruises were – but may include any position from the start of the incident to the end.

In other words, the body remembers that when it was in that position something nasty happened and it had to survive by switching off muscles to protect itself. The body will then remember that position, whether the athlete was conscious or not. If the athlete now puts the body in that position and you test a previously strong indicator, it will go weak.

It is that subconscious memory that will cause hesitancy and lack of confidence on the conscious level. It will still be protecting the athlete in a way that was relevant when the incident happened but isn't relevant now.

HELP

Have the athlete describe the incident in as much detail as possible, getting into the body positions that s/he was in at the time, and test a previously strong indicator muscle. What matters here is not the mental recall so much as the body recall. Any position that causes a weak indicator muscle needs treatment. You may at this point need to support the athlete with cushions or other furniture or equipment relevant to the sport because the position needs to be held while you hold the frontal eminences (ESR points) until the pulses are calm and even (or for 30 seconds if you can't feel any pulse). Retest the indicator muscle. If it is still weak, hold the points some more; if it is now strong, move on to the next position that causes a weak indicator muscle until you have cleared it all out.

Sometimes you get a whole series of positions (like a series of still photographs) and it is possible to re-create an incident which happened when the athlete was unconscious. (While alive, the survival and protective mechanism will always be at work.)

This technique may uncover patterns that have been affecting the body for years, especially in contact sports. However, if the incident has just happened, the athlete *must* be checked by a doctor or hospital first if there is any cause for concern or any change of character, dizziness, unconsciousness – this is normal first-aid practice. Ignore it at your peril. The athlete's life could be in danger.

Sometimes the indicator muscle will not test weak when the athlete is in the position of the accident, especially if it happened long ago and there is no clear conscious memory. You may need to find out how old the athlete was at the time by making the statement: 'You were . . . years old when it happened.' In this case a weak indicator muscle means 'No', a strong indicator means, 'Yes'. If the indicator muscle goes strong at, say, seven years old, the athlete must then think what happened at that age (if the technique hasn't already jogged their memory).

It is useful then to de-stress that incident. While the athlete holds his or her own forehead ESR points, and thinks of him- or herself at that age and about that incident, test all the muscles involved and strengthen them, using the 'help' points for each muscle as appropriate.

When this is complete, make the statement: 'You are now your true age,' and retest the muscles that had been weak at the age the athlete was when the incident happened. Finally, get the athlete into the position that caused the indicator muscle to weaken originally and it should now stay strong, unless there has been further injury or trauma at that site.

ESR – present affirmations and temporal tap

Immediate stress – i.e. someone shouting at the athlete; two attempts gone and only one left; a bad mistake made, but the game's still going – can be helped.

It is not always easy to find a minute or so to practice this technique in the middle of a match, but if you can it will work wonders. These incidents are like super-acute past stress, in that you can only really deal with them after the trigger that caused the stress (although you can make a mental note to plan for the avoidance of further occurrences). Usually the stress is something that has happened in the past and that 'presses your buttons' and makes it all the harder to get it perfectly right now.

HELP

(As though talking directly to the athlete):

Stop (what you are doing if you can). Take some deep breaths, hold the forehead ESR points and review the bit of the technique that failed you. Keep breathing deeply and slowly. Remember a time when you succeeded brilliantly. (Keep holding those points.) Concentrate on how it felt, how it looked. Keep breathing slowly and deeply. Rub the 'help' points to strengthen your muscles, maybe chew a piece of food containing the relevant vitamins, too (rather than chewing gum). Keep breathing deeply and slowly and, remembering the brilliant success and holding the ESR points, start your routine freshly. (It's often quicker to do than read about it here!)

When there is disagreement between the athlete and another player, track official, team mate, etc., it's important to realize that there is always more than one point of view. Take the following example: Sit two people down on opposite sides and put an apple on the table between them. Ask each to describe *exactly* what they see. You will get two descriptions which differ in many small details - how much of the apple is red or green, whether or not the stalk or core is mentioned, whether or not each likes apples anyway, and so on.

The point is that the apple remains unchanged. The descriptions are just two points of view - literally and figuratively. Neither is more right or more wrong. So it is with any situation. Each of us brings a position, a preference, a feeling into the description and thus the conversation. The more you take sides, take positions and dig in, the more there is to defend and consequently the more face there is to lose by giving in, or admitting defeat. Get away from personalities ('you or them') and more into the concerns, fears and aims of both sides. Use sentences like the following:

I see . . . and I imagine . . . and that makes me feel . . ..
What I would like to happen is . . . because . . ..

There must, of course, be agreement by both 'sides' at this point to allow each to tell the truth quietly as they see it, and without fear of interruption!

This is a non-attacking stance that may be alien to an athlete who is geared to winning at all costs. Understanding the other's concerns allows you to give without giving in and losing face and then to move on to a position of working with your previous 'enemy' towards common goals - handling both your concerns.

If you were to test a strong indicator muscle on either the athlete or his apparent opponent immediately before the conversation above the indicator muscle may well go weak. After the conversation it will almost invariably be strong, showing the meeting to have been a helpful and constructive event rather than a confrontation.

Character faults that the athlete may have - like always choking and coming second; being late or forgetting something; or smoking; or anything else that is a habit they can't seem to drop - can be helped by the following technique.

Temporal tap

1 Turn the fault into an affirmation. Instead of the athlete saying things like: I'm no use I always come second; I'm always late, aren't I awful? (a self-fulfilling statement!), get them to turn it into two affirmations:

(a) I can now go on and win.
(b) I no longer need to choke at the last game.
   or
(c) I now always arrive on time.
(d) I no longer need to be late.

2 As the athlete says the first, more positive, version out loud repeatedly, tap the left side of the athlete's head with your right hand, round the ear about 1″ (2.5 cm) away from the ear - starting at the front of the ear and working round to the back of the ear several times over.

3 As the athlete says the second, more negative, version, tap the right side of the athlete's head with your left hand, going round the ear as before, several times. You need both versions to access both halves of the brain. The tapping seems to fix it in the brain.

4 It is sometimes useful to make up a ditty for the athlete to sing to him- or herself. I found the following fitted quite well to the tune of 'Clementine':

I am always in the right place at the right time
And successfully engaged in the right activity.

Barring unavoidable delays caused by accidents (like someone falling under a train), I have almost never been late since. (I used to be constantly late and arrive in a heap. I tried to fit in just one more thing before I left and never allowed for contingencies.) It helped to calm me and get my priorities right and to enjoy being on time.

Planning

It is important for the athlete to bear the following in mind:

(a) There are no failures, only delays.
(b) The plan he or she makes now is not nailed to the wall for ever. They can change it in five minutes' time if they choose.
(c) Have fun, above all. Get them to enjoy running their own life.

The three main factors involved in problem solving and planning are **quality**, **expense** and **time** and it is essential for them to write down *all* the possibilities involved that will help them.

1 First, go back to the WOTS SO list (see page 172) and design some goals for each aspect of the particular sport and the athlete. Turn problems into opportunities and goals. Remove any reference to the word 'but' and replace it with 'and', it's much more positive.
2 Start with long-term goals. If there were no barriers, ask the athlete where in their wildest dreams would their goal be? Name a date five years' hence and write it next to the goal. (Five years is purely arbitrary, but far enough away not to be threatening. Choose a date relevant to their sport.)
3 Now get the athlete to look at that goal in the light of the specific result, main objectives, minor objectives:

   What's the fixture list coming up?
   Major areas to be attacked?
   Who's responsible for each?
   What money, time, effort is needed for each?
   Where's the money coming from?
   Where will the goal be reached?
   What are the risks, what are the 'nuisance and wrecking' factors?
   What is the purpose of each aspect?

4 Decide what would happen if the athlete attacked the chosen goal by:

   Direct opposition.
   Sidestep, tangent or compromise.
   Redefinition (list the barriers and negative thoughts that stopped the athlete before, and when they happened, so they can turn them into affirmations to say to themselves at that time, as they play); change of routine.
   Exaggerating apparent drawbacks - how can the athlete make them work *for* him- or herself?
   Examining the equipment - what's its shape, size, colour, weight, composition (what's it made of), what does it do best/worst?
5 Tell the athlete to rest and relax and to do something else for a while to allow all this information to sink in so that they come back with a fresh mind and fill everything in under the three headings: Quality, Expense, Time.
6 Now they should look at their 'impossible' goal set on the (five year/month) horizon and they should ask themselves these questions:

   (a) to get there, where would you need to be in three years/months?
   (b) to get there, where would you need to be in one year/month?
   (c) to get there, what would you need to accomplish in one week/month from now?

From that decide what you will do by the end of the week and therefore what you will do each day. You have planned the work. Now work the plan.

This technique gives an enormous sense of purpose and yet a relaxed attitude to tomorrow, because the athlete knows they've got that sorted out and there is no fear of forgetting things. Procrastination equals sabotage - but being an enthusiastic athlete this shouldn't be a problem with them!

Remember, if you have both planned wisely now, trust your plan. Don't be tempted to go for the top too early - discuss it together; after all, a coach will be more objective than the athlete. If they have had injuries or other set-backs not allowed for, they may have to re-negotiate their goal date, the quality or quantity of their training, or the amount of time and money they spend. That doesn't matter - they have learned a lesson in self-management that will mean a better plan, and better self-knowledge for the future.

The athlete's objectives change, too, as he or she gets older, better, more experienced. Maybe what seemed an enormous leap forward when they made the plan now seems to them an everyday norm and well within their ability to achieve. The nuts and bolts of the plan are only tools. What is important is the positive sense of command, direction and self-esteem it gives to the athlete.

Visualization

Visualization can take many forms. Basically, it is an experience in imagination and as long as you get the end-result, who cares if the in-between stages are fantastical! This is where you get the athlete to sit on all their logic, all their agonizing analysis and imagine the perfect picture. Read the following to the athlete, slowly.

Sit in a chair (don't lie, you may fall asleep) take some deep breaths, quietly and slowly in and out. Close your eyes and imagine someone is pouring a barrel of pure liquid golden honey over your head. In your mind's eye watch the golden liquid slowly drip and flow in little rivulets down your face, off your nose and then watch it flow down the back of your head, too, down and round your chin and neck, along your shoulders and down your arms, dripping off your fingers, down your back and down your chest. Then as it goes slowly on down put your tongue out and lick your lips – it's so sweet and lovely, this honey. Now take a deep breath, smell the honey scent, and settle back and watch it flowing down. Down, on past your hips, down your thighs, front and back, down to your knees, making little eddies round your knee caps and on down your shins and past your ankles and making a pool round your toes. Breathe slowly and deeply and watch the pool grow and grow till it goes as far as your eyes can see. The world is now bathed in gold. There are golden trees and golden grass and golden sports grounds.

In the golden light now watch the most brilliant technician you've ever seen playing your sport. Watch how they do things, how they feel, where are their feet, hands, arms. See the perfection. Get clear exactly what they are doing. Breathe in and out slowly. Breathe in that perfection. Watch and glory in it.

Now see another figure who is like a carbon copy, doing everything perfectly, too, but you can't see the person's face quite yet. Watch that person, too, and enjoy the feeling, notice the perfect line, the silky technique and perfect timing. Breathe in and out slowly. Breathe in that perfection and smile for that person turns and you see who it is. It is you – and you feel so good, strong, fit and healthy.

Slowly bring yourself back to remembering you are sitting in a chair. Remember what the room looks like where you are, and then open your eyes and smile at the person with you.

Visualizations are always done in the present tense – see it happening *now*. The athlete can invent their own visualization. It will do them all the good in the world to bask in a few moments' peace and perfection. A great advantage is that they will never practice mistakes, so the mind gets used to getting it right!

Now, another technique. Get the athlete to go through the technique mentally in ultra-slow motion, as though watching a slow-motion video. Tell them to watch carefully. Any part of the technique that their mind seems to skip over, is a bit misty and unclear is a part of their technique that needs work. Next tell them to stop the video in their mind and get it clear down to the smallest detail. Then they must rewind the video and run it again. Ask if that spot is clear now? If not it needs more work. If it is, why then, they can exult and move on till they find another bit that's doubtful or unclear.

The athlete should do this technique from the point of view of seeing – in order to really see what each part looks like when it's perfectly done, how simple and effortless it looks. Then they can go back and feel, really feel what each part of the technique feels like when it's perfectly done, how silky smooth and fluent it feels for them. Then they should go back and listen. Listen for perfect timing, perfect contact, perfect rhythm. This should be a sweet sound to them. Now ask them to go back and breathe. They will see how they should breathe for maximum ease and efficiency and they will have lots of energy welling up and to spare to do it even better. Now they must go back and think. The athlete should think each thought for perfect preparation of the next move, think the perfect commands at the perfect time as they move, see, feel, hear and breathe perfection. It will feel beautiful. Any combination that now isn't clear – the athlete must work on it until it is. If it is relevant, add in taste and smell, too. Do it all with love and patience as though you were teaching a child.

Now the athlete's mind has a perfect set of instructions – a blueprint to work with and become closer and closer to – for unless the mind knows precisely what to do, how can it do it? As they improve and know more, the blueprint will become even more skilled and simpler and clearer – and so will they, as a consequence. The athlete can trust that blueprint and use techniques such as 'Inner Game' (see Useful Addresses) if they want to, putting analysis on the shelf and trusting innate knowledge: 'If you know what you are doing, you can do what you want.'

If the athlete finds that visualization is not working well for them, it is possible that they have cranial faults. They might see an osteopath or chiropractor who is an Applied Kinesiologist before trying again.

Goal balancing

It is all very well setting goals – but what if the very idea causes psychological reversals, or the athlete's logical mind says they ought, should, could do it while their emotional mind says it doesn't want to? If this is indeed the case, there is no way they will achieve their goals and what they do gain will be won by very hard effort, for they will be working against themselves.

How to test

First ask the athlete to decide on the goal to be tested. it can be simple like 'I want to win' or 'I want to clear . . . feet.' The athlete stands and then raises both arms out to the side as though for a middle deltoid test each side. He or she repeats stating the goal, while the trainer tests first one arm then the other, pushing it down to the ground. Right arm tests left brain and usually logic; left arm tests right brain and usually emotion. If both were strong before and now one goes weak then there is disagreement between right and left brain – between logically wanting to, but emotionally not wanting to.

HELP

1 The athlete spreads out the hands and imagines right brain lobe in one hand and left brain lobe in the other. Then, while thinking about the goal, the hands are slowly brought together and clasped – to integrate both brain reactions.
2 This method uses acupoints and more muscle testing, but is longer lasting. Test as for the general pain reduction list of muscles (given at the end of Chapter 4) and strengthen any weak ones. Then, while the athlete thinks of the goal, retest and strengthen the ones that are now weak. Retest with the goal in mind. if there is still weakness, find a word that exactly describes the feelings the athlete has about the goal and use ESR techniques to clear it out, using the listed questions in (3) on pages 179-80.

Make sure all the goals on the list are agreeable to both sides of the athlete's brain.

ESR future

This technique will help with future events. Decide what is the worst that can happen, the best that can happen and how it is most likely to happen. De-stress them all by holding the forehead ESR points if any one of them causes a strong indicator muscle to weaken. Write down all the repetitive negative thoughts you have as you play or compete, such as, 'Can I make it?' 'Why is it always uphill?' 'I'm doing more harm than good', etc. and de-stress them, too.

It may be a good idea for the athlete to find out as

much as possible about their opponents, the venue, where essential support services are (lavatory, restaurant, changing rooms, equipment repair facilities, physios, sleeping arrangements, etc.) – even tell them to go there a few days before, if necessary, on a reconnoitre mission, or at least to get there really early. The athlete should rehearse in their mind exactly what it will feel like, sound, smell and taste like and where and when they will warm up, what their practical and mental routine will be, what commands they will give themselves and when or at what landmarks to psyche themselves up or calm down as need be. If any of these bother them in any way (because they arrived early or are rehearsing this in their mind), they should de-stress by sitting, thinking, breathing deeply and holding their forehead ESR points. Then they think of sailing through with total ease and everything falling into place. The athlete should breathe slowly again, holding the forehead ESR points till they are quite clear how easy it will all be, remembering they can always ask for the support they need. Sport is not a life and death matter – it's supposed to be *fun*!

Having de-stressed the worst, the best and the most likely – why not go for the best?

The Muscle Test – How does it work?

By *Rodney Adeniyi-Jones*

Manual muscle testing as used in Applied Kinesiology is a test of the neurological *control* of the muscle function, not a test of its absolute strength.

Muscle strength testing procedures have long been part of standard neurological assessment, to evaluate damage to the brain, nerves or muscles.[1] [2] Strength is graded from zero (no movement at all) to grade 5 (full strength – the ability to move against gravity and resistance). Kinesiology testing assesses variation in the control of normal strength (grade 5) muscles.

The mechanism of the muscle test is the modulation of the basic spinal reflex arc.[3] Pressure on the hand causes the muscle to stretch. This is sensed by the proprioceptive (spindle) cell in the muscle which sends the information to the spinal cord. The information passes to the motor part of the spinal cord and a reflex contraction of the muscle occurs, causing the arm to maintain its position. This is perceived as a 'strong' muscle test. Any factors that delay or inhibit the reflex contraction of the muscle will make the test appear 'weak'. Many neurological factors influence this reflex arc; they include messages from the brain, from the cerebellum, from other limbs and from joints. To this well-known list, kinesiological research adds: electromagnetic fields, acupuncture meridian energy,[4] tastes, smells, homoeopathic remedy energies and psychological states.

The majority of the recent research into Applied Kinesiology has been done by members of the International College of Applied Kinesiology, the professional body that governs standards, training and procedures, as well as research into muscle testing.

Not surprisingly, objective measures of muscle strength do not correlate with the findings of manual muscle testing.[5] Work has been done using the Cybex II dynamometer, and one of the most experienced groups in the field, Nicholas *et al*[6] state: 'What is measured manually cannot be measured by the Cybex alone'. This is because mechanical testing equipment does not *apply* force to the muscle as is done in the manual test; therefore the sensory (proprioceptive) and co-ordination elements of the manual test are missing. The *rate of application* of the test force is also crucial.[7] [8] Hand-held pressure transducers currently offer one of the most promising avenues of study,[9] [10] [11] but much of the work done so far has concentrated on strength and failed to take into account the rate of application of the force.

The ability of different testers (or indeed the same tester) to obtain the same results reliably depends, as in many fields, on the skill and knowledge of the tester. Agreement between testers who did not know each other's results rose from 78.2 per cent to 100 per cent in one study[12] as increasing degrees of error prevention were applied. In another study, without the error prevention measures, there was 81.9 per cent agreement.[13]

APPENDIX REFERENCES

1   American Medical Association, members' *Guide to the Evaluation of Permanent Impairment*, 2nd Ed. (Chicago: AMA, 1984)

2   Kendall, F.P. and McCreary, E.K. *Muscles – Testing and Function*, 3rd Ed. (Baltimore: Williams & Wilkins, 1983)

3   Sherrington, C. *The Integrative Activity of the Nervous System*, (Cambridge: Cambridge University Press, 1947)

4   Goodheart, G. 'Chinese Lessons for Chiropractic', *Chiropractic Economics*, 8, 5 (1966)

5   Blaich, R.M. and Mendenhall, E.I. 'Manual Muscle Testing and Cybex Machine Muscle Testing: a Search for a Correlation.' Proceedings of Winter Meeting, International College of Applied Kinesiology, San Diego, 1983

6   Nicholas, J.A., Strizak, A.M. *et al*, 'A Study of Thigh Muscle Weakness in Different Pathological States of the Lower Extremity', *American Journal of Sports Medicine*, 4, 6 (1976)

7   Ryan, A.H. and Agnew, J.H. 'Studies in Muscular Power and Fatigue', *American Journal of Physiology*, 42 (1917)

8   Nicholas, A.J. *et al*, 'Factors influencing Manual Muscle Tests in Physical Therapy – the magnitude and duration of force applied', *Journal of Bone and Joint Surgery*, 60A, 2 (March 1978)

9   Bohannon, R.W. 'Test-retest Reliability of Hand-held Dynamometry during a Single Session of Strength Assessment', *Physical Therapy*, 66, 2 (February 1986)

10   Marino, M. *et al*, 'The Efficacy of Manual Assessment of Muscle Strength using a New Device', *American Journal of Sports Medicine*, 10, 6 (1982)

11   Nicholas, J.A., Melvin, M. *et al*, 'Neurophysiologic Inhibition of Strength following Tactile Stimulation of the Skin', *American Journal of Sports Medicine*, 8, 3 (1980)

12   Conable, K.M. and Hanick, B.T. *Interexaminer Agreement in Applied Kinesiology Muscle Testing.* Selected Papers of the International College of Applied Kinesiology, ed. D.H. Schusterman (Shawnee Mission KS: ICAK, 1987)

13   Jacobs, G.E. 'Applied Kinesiology: An experimental evaluation by double blind methodology', *Journal of Manipulative Physiological Therapy*, 4, 3 (September 1981)

Bibliography

Barton, John, *The Encyclopedia of Mind and Body Atlas*, Vols 1-8

Beardall, Alan, *Clinical Kinesiology*, Vols I-V

Fisher, Roger and Ury, William, *Getting to Yes*, Penguin Books

Gallwey, W. Timothy, *The Inner Game of Tennis*, Jonathan Cape

Grisogono, Vivianne, *Sports Injuries*, John Murray

Lebowitz, Michael, *Body Mechanics*, MMI Press, Harrisville, NH 03450

Mervyn, Leonard, *Thorsons Complete Guide to Vitamins and Minerals*, Thorsons Publishing Group

Pritikin, Nathan, *Diet for Runners*, Bantam

Read, Malcom and Wade, Paul, *Sports Injuries*, Brestick & Fess

Stonor, Fred, *The Eclectic Approach to Chiropractic*, FLS Publishing, USA

Syer, John and Connolly, Christopher, *Sporting Body, Sporting Mind*, Cambridge University Press

Thie, John, *Touch for Health*, De Vorss & Co., 1046 Princeton Drive, Marina del Ray, California 90291

Walther, David S., *Applied Kinesiology*, Vols. I and II, Systems DL

Walther, David S., *Applied Kinesiology: Synopsis*, Systems DL

Lecture Notes

Sheldon Deal 1983-9

Dr Adeniyi-Jones 1989

Wendy Wallace Clinical Psychologist 1988

Werner Erhardt Associates

For additional research of all Applied Kinesiology information, please consult *ICAK Selected Papers* (ed. D.H. Schusterman), Shawnee Mission, Kansas State, USA

Index